OUTSIDE THE BOX

FOR AGES
9-11

MOLLY POTTER

A&C BLACK

With thanks to...
Andy the great man behind the woman.
Mikey, Jed and Maddy for playing with me and keeping
my imagination alive.
Claire for helping me to appear like I'm coming from inside the box at
crucial times in my life.
Jackie Frost for teaching me everything I know.
Paul Stanley for a teaching perspective from inside the box.
Mum and Dad for not keeping me in a box!

Published 2007 by A & C Black Publishers Ltd
38 Soho Square, London W1D 3HB
www.acblack.com
ISBN 978-0-7136-8145-1
Written by Molly Potter
Design by Cathy Tincknell
Illustration by John Kelly
Copyright © A & C Black Publishers Ltd

Printed in Great Britain by Caligraving Ltd, Thetford, Norfolk

A & C Black uses paper produced with elemental chlorine-free pulp,
harvested from managed sustainable forests.

To see our full range of books
visit **www.acblack.com**

Contents

INTRODUCTION   4

SECTION 1 - DESIGN   6
Signs   6
Difficult food   8
Museum of the Mozteks   10
An environment   12
A new sport   14
Design a flower   16
Design a restaurant   18

SECTION 2 – CREATIVE THINKING   20
Ten Star Hotel for kids   20
Disastrous Desmond   22
Badge book   24
Modelling fun!   26
Your perfect remote control   28
A roog   30
School exchange   32
Win the golden tokens   34

SECTION 2 – EXPLORING LANGUAGE   36
Promote your band!   36
A revolting menu   38
School report   40
World's worst- World's best   42
Do a double take!   44
One glitful day   46

SECTION 2 – PROBLEM SOLVING   48
Gloomsville   48
The Mystery of the Bronze Globe   50
Murder mystery   52
Place the pylons   54
Four letters   56
Design a park   58
Bundy's Activity Park   60
Whigby   62

Introduction

How this book is organised

The activities in this book have been organised into four sections based on their main focus but because of the nature of creativity there is inevitably some degree of overlap. The sections are: Design, Creative thinking, Exploring language and Problem solving. As each activity is stand alone, there is no prescribed order for doing them so selection of an activity is entirely up to you, depending on the skills you would like to develop and the nature and capability of the class you are working with. It is recommended that you make sure children thoroughly understand the task from the outset to ensure they know what to do and how to do it. Once underway, pupils usually become embroiled and need little supervision.

Each activity consists of a double page spread. The first page is teachers' notes outlining the task and what is involved. Additional background information is also provided where necessary. The accompanying pupil's page is designed to be photocopied and handed out to the class but for some of the activities you will also need to provide spare paper.

Suggests the size of group that would be suitable for the task.

Indicates the approximate time required to do the task.

Summarises the task

Outlines how to introduce the task.

Provides answers, ideas, guidance and further information to help you get the most out of the activity.

Suggests extension activities that can be used to expand the project or to provide activities for pupils who finish early. (Some of these extension ideas can lengthen a project considerably and would require a lot more time than indicated at the top of the page.)

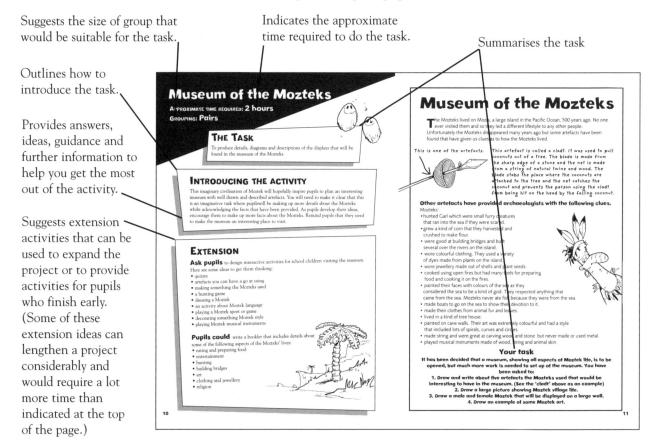

When to use the activities

Any of the activities can be used at any time during the school year. They can be used:

- As a quirky way of starting the new term and getting to know a new class
- At the end of term or after SATs when the timetable is more relaxed
- For the remaining members of a year group that have not been able to go on a school trip
- If someone is taking the whole year group at short notice or to cover PPA time
- To provide something different that will make sure everyone is involved in an exciting and thought provoking task.

Why use this book?

There is no doubt from recent educational developments that creativity is making a come back! The National Advisory Committee report by the DfES 'All our futures: creativity, culture and education,' states that, 'we are all, or can be, creative to a lesser or greater degree if we are given the opportunity'. This is what the activities in this book set out to do – to give children the chance to be creative by providing inspirational starting points to help them stretch their minds and problem solve. In the same report, creativity is defined as having four components:

- Imagination
- Purpose
- Originality
- Value i.e. has the purpose been met?

With the problems posed and tasks set in this book, pupils have opportunities to employ all four of the above in discrete, one-off activities. Using the ideas in the book, will also mean that creativity is not left entirely within the 'arts' curriculum' as is so often the case in many UK primary schools.

So why is creativity so important?

The QCA's 'Creativity, Find it and Promote it' website describes how promoting pupil's creativity can:

- Improve self esteem, motivation and achievement
- Develop skills for adult life
- Develop the talent of the individual

If the activities in this book help to develop and foster any one of the attributes of 'The creative child' as shown below then this book will be well on the road to achieving its goal!

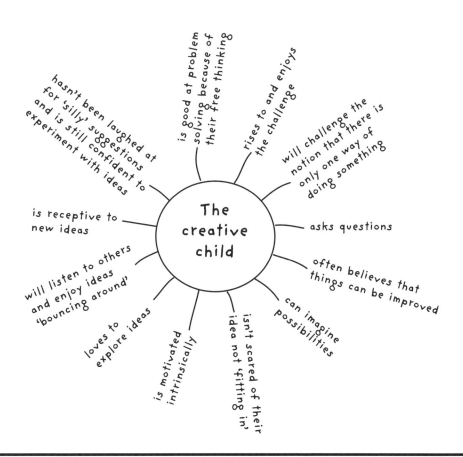

The creative child
- is good at problem solving because of their free thinking
- rises to and enjoys the challenge
- will challenge the notion that there is only one way of doing something
- asks questions
- often believes that things can be improved
- can imagine possibilities
- isn't scared of their idea not 'fitting in'
- is motivated intrinsically
- loves to explore ideas
- will listen to others and enjoy ideas 'bouncing around'
- is receptive to new ideas
- hasn't been laughed at for 'silly' suggestions and is still confident to experiment with ideas

Signs

APPROXIMATE TIME REQUIRED: **1 hour**

GROUPING: **Individuals**

THE TASK

To design and draw (or paint) serious and comical signs using the format of British road signs.

INTRODUCING THE ACTIVITY

Start by reminding pupils about the need for road signs to be simple, clear and with little or no writing on them. Pupils need to remember that orders are usually in circle-shaped signs, information in rectangular-shaped signs and warnings in triangular-shaped signs. They could spend time looking at existing road signs and guessing what they mean to help familiarise themselves with the style of design.

Orders
(circular)

Information
(often rectangular or square)

Warnings
(triangular)

Allow the pupils to choose as many of the signs to design as they like to start with but it's quite good to give them a minimum number that they should complete. They could go on to paint a bigger version of their favourite sign that could be used in the school building or the classroom.

EXTENSION

Pupils could:

- Think of some signs they might like to have up at home.
- Devise a multiple choice quiz of what existing road signs mean.
- Make up some signs and ask people to guess what they think the signs mean.
- Draw a street map and make suggestions about the road signs you might see in different positions.

Signs

Your task

Design signs for some of the warnings, information and orders below. Choose one or two of your favourite designs to enlarge.

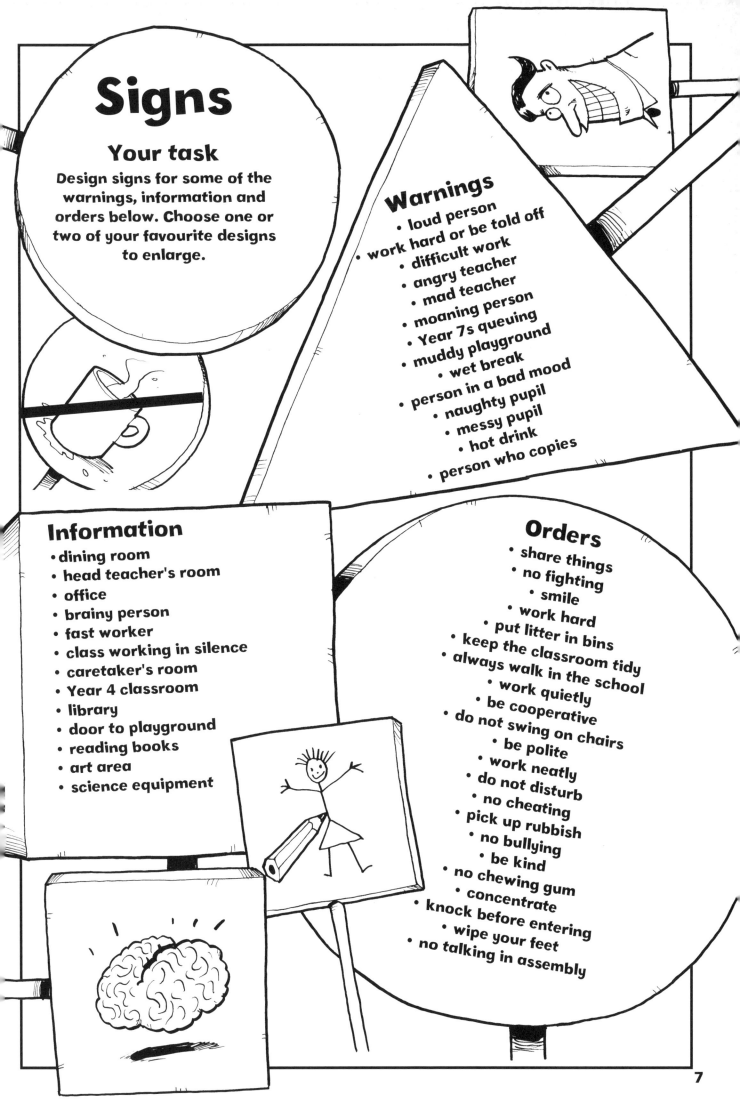

Warnings

- loud person
- work hard or be told off
- difficult work
- angry teacher
- mad teacher
- moaning person
- Year 7s queuing
- muddy playground
- wet break
- person in a bad mood
- naughty pupil
- messy pupil
- hot drink
- person who copies

Information

- dining room
- head teacher's room
- office
- brainy person
- fast worker
- class working in silence
- caretaker's room
- Year 4 classroom
- library
- door to playground
- reading books
- art area
- science equipment

Orders

- share things
- no fighting
- smile
- work hard
- put litter in bins
- keep the classroom tidy
- always walk in the school
- work quietly
- be cooperative
- do not swing on chairs
- be polite
- work neatly
- do not disturb
- no cheating
- pick up rubbish
- no bullying
- be kind
- no chewing gum
- concentrate
- knock before entering
- wipe your feet
- no talking in assembly

Difficult food

APPROXIMATE TIME REQUIRED: **1 hour**

GROUPING: **Individuals or pairs**

THE TASK

To draw labelled designs for utensils that will help people eat the 'difficult' food.

INTRODUCING THE ACTIVITY

Encourage pupils to try and make it as easy as possible to eat the difficult food. Pupils' ideas will vary considerably in detail and feasibility! For less able pupils, a different selection of food could be chosen, possibly including some from the list below.

Rucket – has to be coaxed by something red on to a rod, which it will wind itself around.

Chowper – a powder that can only be eaten if ALL of the powder is taken off the plate at the same time. It needs to be kept together otherwise it puffs into the air and escapes.

Tagu – extremely slippery and slimy and will slime its way to the ground unless no part of it can 'see' the ground.

Tarrapod – wafer like food that crumbles and floats away unless it is spun whilst being lifted.

Rass – balls that roll around on the plate and can only be caught in a net, strictly two at a time.

Sausass – a long thick cylinder shaped food (2cm in diameter and 15cm in length that has to be squashed lengthways down to 8cm before it can be eaten.

Hookray – a food that has a hook growing out of its top. It has to be eaten by being lifted vertically (it must be straight up or it unhooks and fall sideways to the floor) and eaten straight above the point at which it left the plate.

Kratter – spiky food that bounces (always away from the plate!).

Smelf – blue and yellow paste that has to be mixed in equal amounts to make a green paste before eating.

EXTENSION

Pupils could also:

- Produce the packaging for a complete utensil set. Encourage them to make their utensils stylish, perhaps all with the same handle design. Instructions for using the utensils could also be included.
- Design a magazine advert for the utensils.
- Design a TV advert for the utensils (can be very funny).
- Design plates that will help with each of the foods.
- Write the descriptions on how to prepare each of the foods – for the side of the packet.
- Make up their own difficult food and put it on a menu.

Difficult food

Your task

The following food is only served in restaurants in Karamania. The problem is that people love eating this food because it is so delicious but it is extremely awkward to eat, especially as you cannot touch it with your hands. You are needed to design the utensils (like knives, spoons and forks) that will make eating this food easier.

Haff

Haff is a delicious feathery food that floats above the plate and if hands get closer than 40cm it is attracted to and sticks to them.

Masmer

Masmer is really tasty. It is magnetic, but only when it has been tickled by a feather. Masmer can only be picked up by metal.

Plipper

Plipper is a scrumptious seaweed that is rather like bubblewrap. To get the full flavour, each of the bubbles must be popped by a pin prick.

Glat

Glat is a yummy food that is full of juice. Before it can be eaten, however, a lot of the juice must be squeezed out of it.

Ragetti

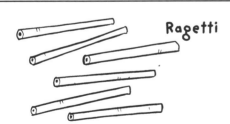

Ragetti is shaped like spaghetti but every piece is always 6cm long. Ragetti needs to be cut into 2cm pieces before it can be eaten.

Springling

Springling is an appetising food shaped like a spring. It can only be eaten by squashing the spring and then letting it go so that hopefully it lands in your mouth.

Museum of the Mozteks

APPROXIMATE TIME REQUIRED: 2 hours

GROUPING: Pairs

THE TASK

To produce details, diagrams and descriptions of the displays that will be found in the Museum of the Mozteks.

INTRODUCING THE ACTIVITY

This imaginary civilisation of Moztek will hopefully inspire pupils to plan an interesting museum with well drawn and described artefacts. You will need to make it clear that this is an imaginative task where pupils will be making up more details about the Mozteks while acknowledging the facts that have been provided. As pupils develop their ideas, encourage them to make up more facts about the Mozteks. Remind pupils that they need to make the museum an interesting place to visit.

EXTENSION

Ask pupils to design interactive activities for school children visiting the museum. Here are some ideas to get them thinking:

- quizzes
- artefacts you can have a go at using
- making something the Mozteks used
- a hunting game
- dressing as a Moztek
- an activity about Moztek language
- playing a Moztek sport or game
- decorating something in Moztek style
- playing Moztek musical instruments

Pupils could write a booklet that includes details about some of the following aspects of the Mozteks' lives:

- eating and preparing food
- entertainment
- hunting
- building bridges
- art
- clothing and jewellery
- religion

Museum of the Mozteks

The Mozteks lived on Mozia, a large island in the Pacific Ocean, 500 years ago. No one ever visited them and so they led a different lifestyle to any other people. Unfortunately the Mozteks disappeared many years ago but some artefacts have been found that have given us clues as to how the Mozteks lived.

This is one of the artefacts.

This artefact is called a cladt. It was used to pull coconuts out of a tree. The blade is made from the sharp edge of a stone and the net is made from a string of natural twine and wood. The blade stabs the place where the coconuts are attached to the tree and the net catches the coconut and prevents the person using the cladt from being hit on the head by the falling coconut.

Other artefacts have provided archaeologists with the following clues.

Mozteks:

- hunted garl which were small furry creatures that ran into the sea if they were scared.
- grew a kind of corn that they harvested and crushed to make flour.
- were good at building bridges and built several over the rivers on the island.
- wore colourful clothing. They used a variety of dyes made from plants on the island.
- wore jewellery made out of shells and plant seeds.
- cooked using open fires but had many tools for preparing food and cooking it on the fires.
- painted their faces with colours of the sea as they considered the sea to be a kind of god. They respected anything that came from the sea. Mozteks never ate fish because they were from the sea.
- made boats to go on the sea to show their devotion to it.
- made their clothes from animal fur and leaves.
- lived in a kind of tree house.
- painted on cave walls. Their art was extremely colourful and had a style that included lots of spirals, curves and circles.
- made string and were great at carving wood and stone but never made or used metal.
- played musical instruments made of wood, string and animal skin.

Your task

It has been decided that a museum, showing all aspects of Moztek life, is to be opened, but much more work is needed to set up the museum. You have been asked to:

1. Draw and write about five artefacts the Mozteks used that would be interesting to have in the museum. (See the 'cladt' above as an example).

2. Draw a large picture showing Moztek village life.

3. Draw a male and female Moztek that will be displayed on a large wall.

4. Draw an example of some Moztek art.

An environment

APPROXIMATE TIME REQUIRED: 1 hour

GROUPING: Individuals

THE TASK

To design living things that could exist in a specific environment.

INTRODUCING THE ACTIVITY

Most pupils get their teeth stuck into this activity readily but they do need to be reminded that their creature and plant designs need to include features that will help them survive in this environment.

Discuss survival features to remind pupils before they embark upon their designs.

Plants: need water, nutrients from the soil, sunlight and air. More able pupils could consider how their plant will be successfully pollinated (by wind or insect) and how the seeds produced by the plant will be transported away from the parent plant (by wind, animal or other means).

Plant eaters: need water, need to be able to see all around them so they can still eat but watch out for movement of their predators, need teeth that can chew plants, need to be camouflaged so they can hide from predators, need something that might protect them from predators or put predators off eating them, need to be able to eat lots of plants.

Meat eaters: need water, need to be camouflaged so they can creep up on their prey, need a way of catching their prey. It's a good idea to suggest that their animal designs look something like an animal (with features like legs, fur, trunks, ears, teeth, tails, etc) and not like an alien! You may like to point out to the pupils that when they have finished the task they will have drawn a complete food chain for the environment i.e.

Plant ⟶ Plant eater (Herbivore) ⟶ Meat eater (Carnivore)

EXTENSION

Pupils could:

- Design an environment of their own and then design the plants and animals that live there. They will need to consider what each of the following are like:

    - rocks   - weather
    - trees   - temperature
    - insects   - any existing plants
    - soil   - where water can be found
    - light   - any other special features like the sand mounds and slime pits

- Design a tent that would be suitable for humans staying in this environment. It would need to keep the people using it safe and comfortable.

An environment

This is a cold environment with strong winds.

Light leaves the sun in strips and moves around slowly.

SUN

tree

green slime pit

three winged insect

holes down which water can be found

yellow rock

red soil

blue sand mounds

bushy cotton wool plant

Your task

1. You are going to design a plant that could live in this environment. Remember that plants need water, light and air to grow and nutrients from the soil to remain healthy. Try also to work out how your plant will be pollinated and how the plant makes sure that its seeds move away from the parent plant so they do not grow in its shadow.

2. You are going to design an animal that survives by eating the plant that you design. Remember that it needs to be able to get water and eat a lot of the plant. The animal needs to avoid being eaten by the meat-eating animal you are going to design in tasks 3.

3. You are also going to design an animal that eats the animal that eats the plant. Remember that it needs to be able to drink water and catch the animal it eats.

For tasks 2 and 3 think about:
teeth • camouflage • position of the eyes • where it lives
sense of smell • how it moves • how it keeps warm
can the animal defend itself? • any other features that help it survive

A new sport

APPROXIMATE TIME REQUIRED: **1 hour**

GROUPING: **Individuals, pairs or threes**

THE TASK

To complete details about partially described new sports and to make up a completely new sport.

INTRODUCING THE ACTIVITY

You could start by asking pupils to list as many sports as they can think of (e.g. hockey, netball, football, rugby, athletics, archery, swimming, running, skiing, sailing, darts, judo) and then choose one of these sports to give details of using the same format as the cards on the pupils' page i.e. name, number of players, skills involved etc. You could also ask pupils to list the skills that different sports require.

Read through the sheet and consider the three sports. These have some details about them that are missing. Ask pupils to complete the missing details for these three sports by inventing them. Give pupils some scrap paper to note down their ideas so that they can feedback to the rest of the class.

Then ask pupils to consider inventing a new sport from scratch. Pupils can use the headings on the cards on the sheet (Name, Number of players, Skills involved...etc) to help outline information about their sport. If pupils really struggle, explain that they can keep the idea really simple by making it a very straightforward sport e.g. an aiming, jumping or a timing sport. Once pupils have discussed and decided upon their sport's details, ask them to write a fact sheet about their new sport – including all the details on the cards, pictures of people doing the sport, pictures of the equipment and any court or pitch markings and clothing (including protective gear) worn to do the sport.

You can help prompt pupils with the following notes:

Name: Pupils might like to mix syllables from two different sports or make up a completely new word.

Number of players: consider whether the sport tests an individual's skill one at a time like archery or if it has 2,3,4 or 5 players or a team of a set number on each side.

Skills involved: balancing, batting, catching, throwing, running, manoeuvring, speed, stamina, calculation, dexterity, anticipation, hitting, aiming, strength, controlled movement, jumping, keeping something from the ground etc.

Equipment: lines painted on the ground, hoops, nets, bats, balls (what size and shape?), beanbags, buckets, targets, poles, ropes, benches, pitches, courts, walls, cones, posts, wickets, sticks, goals etc.

How do you play? Ask pupils to be as clear as possible with their descriptions.

How do you score? There might be just a score for achieving something, or a timing that you have to beat or a more complicated scoring (like in badminton – only the server can score).

How do you win? Arrive at a score, arrive at a number of points more than your opponent, beat your opponent, take the least time to do something, make the least mistakes?

EXTENSION

Pupils draw and explain a 'Super Obstacle Course' that aims to test several of the above skills.

A new sport

Your task

Here are some unfinished details about some new sports. Your task is to make up the missing details and then make up an imaginary sport of your own.

1

Name:

Number of players: 2

Skills involved: Speed, manoeuvring, throwing.

Equipment: A small walled-in court with a low net across the middle of it, eight bean bags.

How do you play? You start with four bean bags each — one in each corner of your half of the court. You continuously throw your bean bags into your opponent's side of the court.

How do you score? You score one point if at any point in time all the bean bags are in your opponent's side of the court.

How do you win? The first person to score 5.

2

Name:

Number of players: Up to 15 but only one 'in play' at a time, the others are all fielders.

Skills involved:

Equipment: One very bouncy ball, a position marked in the centre of a large circle (diameter 10 metres) painted on the ground.

How do you play? The 'player' stands on the dot in the centre of the circle and throws the ball out, trying to touch the ground for two bounces, on the ground, outside the circle, without the fielders catching it. Three fielders' catches in a row gets the player out and the last catcher takes the player's place.

How do you score?

How do you win?

3

Name:

Number of players:

Skills involved: Throwing, aiming, speed.

Equipment: A large, vertical hoop (diameter — 3 metres) standing 2 metres off the ground in the centre of a court, a sponge ball.

How do you play?

How do you score?

How do you win?

Design a flower

APPROXIMATE TIME REQUIRED: 1 hour

GROUPING: Individuals

THE TASK

To design a flower for Fred (the insect provided) to pollinate.

This activity can be used to revise pollination. It's up to you how 'realistic' the design should be but as it's meant to be a fun activity, allowing the odd ladder or signpost in the design doesn't stop pupils from learning about pollination!

INTRODUCING THE ACTIVITY

Start by revising the process of pollination so that everyone is very clear about what needs to happen. The process of pollination can really be simplified into:

Pollen from the anther of one flower lands on the stigma of another flower.

Stress to pupils the idea that it is much better for the plant if it does not self-pollinate. Ask pupils to think of ways of preventing this in the flower they are going to design. Pupils might manage this by:

- designing the flower so that Fred can only travel in one direction so that he has to brush any pollen off his back (from the previous flower he visited) onto the stigma of one flower before picking up the pollen of that flower.
- using a trap door that only swings one way.
- using clear arrows telling Fred which way to go.
- inventing more elaborate ways of preventing self pollination!

Pupils also need to take into account the fact that Fred can't fly, so the flower either needs to droop down or it needs to have a means by which Fred can climb up to the flower.

EXTENSION

Pupils could:

- Attempt to make their design with art straws and card.
- Design seeds that can be removed from the parent plant effectively by wind or by animals.

Design a flower

Just to remind you...

Pollination is where pollen from a flower's anther lands on the stigma of another plant. Flowers can be pollinated by the wind and by insects. It is better for the plant if pollen from a flower does not land on its own stigma and pollinate itself (self-pollination). Pollen (from insect pollinated plants) is a very fine sticky powder that sticks to insects' hairs.

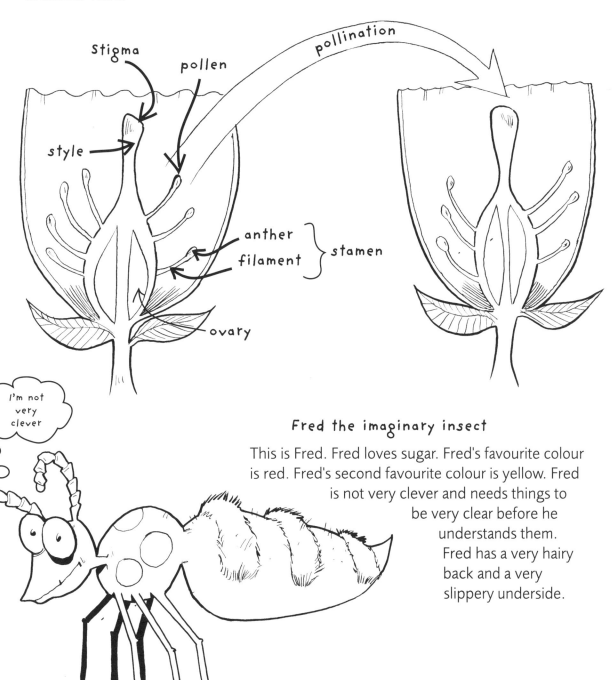

Fred the imaginary insect

This is Fred. Fred loves sugar. Fred's favourite colour is red. Fred's second favourite colour is yellow. Fred is not very clever and needs things to be very clear before he understands them. Fred has a very hairy back and a very slippery underside.

Your task

Design a flower for Fred to pollinate. See if you can make a design that will stop Fred self-pollinating the flower. Label the anther, the stigma, and all other parts of your flower.

Design a restaurant

APPROXIMATE TIME REQUIRED: 4 hours

GROUPING: Groups of three

To plan the design and running of a successful restaurant.

INTRODUCING THE ACTIVITY

Pupils could start by thinking of restaurants or cafés that they have been to and what they liked or did not like about them. Ask pupils what is/are the main reason/s for a person deciding to go to a restaurant. They will probably consider the menu as most important. Other considerations might be the atmosphere, cleanliness, décor, any special offers, friendliness and efficiency of the staff and how well it has been advertised. Make it clear to pupils that they need to design their restaurant in a way that will make it most likely to be a success.

Encourage pupils to think about an overall style for their restaurant and whether or not they are going to have a theme that runs through the décor and menu, but tell pupils this is not always necessary, as a good menu and pleasant décor can be enough to get the customers in. Encourage pupils to compile all their work as if it were a business proposal to be judged once it's finished. They can decide whether they want to present it in a folder or as a poster.

When the plans has been completed, pupils can present their work to the rest of the class who could assess the restaurant design, giving marks out of ten for the following categories:

Category	Detail	Mark (out of 10)
Restaurant sign	Name of restaurant	
	Design of sign	
Decoration of the building	Wallpaper/pictures/curtains/furniture	
	Colour scheme	
	Table decoration	
Arrangement of restaurant	Practicality	
Menu	Choice	
	Design of menu	
Promotion of restaurant	Flyer (advert)	
Overall	Would you want to eat in the restaurant?	
Extras	Any further ideas/work	
	Total	

JOE'S CAF
spheshuls

EXTENSION

- Pupils could make a radio advert for their restaurant.
- See also suggestions on the pupils' activity sheet.

Design a restaurant

Your task

You have just bought a run-down building that you are going to turn into a restaurant. You really want your restaurant to be a success. Before you can open, however, you have a lot of work to do.

Here is the list of things you need to do:

- **Name your restaurant**: Decide what to call your restaurant and draw a design of the sign that will go above the front of it.

- **Decor**: Draw a picture of what you intend the restaurant to look like inside after you have decorated it. Draw a picture of a wall and one table, set up as it will look just before you open. Don't forget to choose tasteful colours to paint the walls, pictures to go on the walls, and fine details like tablecloths and perhaps a vase of flowers on the table.

- **Map it out**: Draw a plan (bird's eye view) of the restaurant showing where the kitchen, the toilets and all the tables will go.

- **Menu**: Decide what you are going to have on your menu. Remember starters, main meals, desserts, and drinks. You could have extra sections on your menu like light snacks or 'today's specials'. Design and draw the menu that you have decided on.

- **Advertise**: Write a flyer that could be printed and posted through letterboxes to advertise your new restaurant.

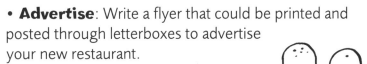

Extension

- **Write your waiter's job description. A job description tells a person that you have employed exactly what you expect them to do as part of their job.**
- **Draw what your restaurant will look like from outside (the shop front).**
- **Write a questionnaire for your new customers that would give you an idea of what they like and didn't like about your new restaurant.**
- **Think about any special promotions that you could organise to encourage new customers into your restaurant. You could include live music or two meals for the price of one etc. Make sure the offers don't mean that you end up taking very little money from the customer and try and make the promotion interesting and original (not like the examples given!).**
- **Draw a few of the meals on your menu to show the cook what you hope the meals will look like.**

Ten Star Hotel for kids

APPROXIMATE TIME REQUIRED: 3 hours

GROUPING: Pairs or groups of three

THE TASK

To put forward the best ideas for a luxury and fun hotel for children.

INTRODUCING THE ACTIVITY

Explain that they are working in teams and that the winning team will be the team with the best ideas for the way the hotel would be set up. Explain that they need to come up with really unusual and fun ideas to win.

Explain to pupils that the hotel ideas need to be realistic. You can't defy gravity, travel in time or transport people through air for example! Ask pupils to start by listing all the things they think they would like to include in their hotel.

Ask pupils to produce the following:

1. A name for the hotel.
2. A description and picture of the foyer and what happens there. Explain to pupils that you would want the foyer to have impact and to give a very startling first impression.
3. A picture (with labels) of how the children will get to their rooms.
4. A picture and description of one of the rooms with all fun and luxurious features labelled and described.
5. A list and description of all the other things that children can do while they are staying in the hotel. This could be produced in a leaflet format.

Pupils then need to present their proposals to the rest of the class and the class can vote to decide which hotel they think they would most like to stay in.

EXTENSION
Pupils could:
- Design a brochure for the 'winning' hotel proposal.
- Consider the staff this hotel would need to employ and list all the jobs that would need doing.

Ten Star Hotel for kids

Your task

You have been asked to help change a large, run down hotel into a ten star hotel for kids. This will be an absolutely luxurious and fun experience for any child that comes to stay in this hotel. The people who will be running the hotel are going to advertise it to encourage nine to eleven year olds to stay there. It costs a lot of money to stay in this hotel but once a child has paid, everything inside is free.

What you need to consider:

1. The name of your hotel
• What would be a really good name for such a hotel?
• Will the name some how tell you that the hotel is luxurious and for children?

2. The hotel's foyer
• What will children be greeted by when they first walk into the hotel?
• How will the children book into the hotel?
• What will any staff in the foyer do?
• How will the children be told of all the things they can do in the hotel?

3. The route to the bedrooms
• Will there be a lift or some other form of transport?
• Will it be a fun journey?

4. The bedrooms
• What will the beds be like in the rooms?
• What will the view be like from the window (any special features here)?
• What luxurious and fun things will be included in the rooms?
• What will the bathroom be like?
• How will the children be able to get anything they need and what might be on offer?

5. Other activities in the hotel
• In the other parts of the hotel, what will the children also be able to find?
• What sports and games will be available in the hotel?
• Will there be a swimming pool and what will it be like?
• What eating places will there be in the hotel?
• What services will the staff offer?

Disastrous Desmond

APPROXIMATE TIME REQUIRED: 1 hour
GROUPING: Individuals, pairs or groups of 3 or 4

THE TASK

To think creatively and entertainingly about a disastrous character.

INTRODUCING THE ACTIVITY

This activity can actually set the class off giggling! It can be set as a competition to create the most Disastrous Desmond! Pupils can work individually, but pupils working in pairs, or even small groups of mixed abilities, can help to get the ideas flowing.

1. It is a good idea to start off with task one as a whole class to really get pupils into the idea of just how disastrous Desmond is.

2. Ask pupils to try and include as many disastrous details as possible. You could ask pupils to draw Desmond with six clues to (or evidence of) a disaster he has had. Some examples:
- spaghetti on his top
- a cut knee
- odd shoes
- a parking ticket
- a ripped pair of trousers
- a shrunken top
- a bruise on his forehead
- a plaster cast
- mud up his leg
- a dog lead round his waist…etc

3. Pupils could draw Desmond's journey as a cartoon if they prefer. Again encourage them to think of as many disasters as possible. Some ideas to start them off:
- getting lost
- falling over
- cutting himself
- getting muddled
- buying the wrong thing
- going to the wrong shop
- forgetting something
- catching a bus when he wasn't meant to
- trying to push a door that should be pulled and breaking it
- dropping the milk
- the newspaper blowing off in the wind
- causing other people to have disasters

4. With this task you need to encourage pupils to discuss the details of the things that make them really disastrous e.g. Desmond might have a dog as a pet but that this is only disastrous when the details about the dog are added i.e. the moment the dog is put on a lead he runs around his owner and ties his legs up. He licks all food…etc. Pupils could choose two or three of the ideas that inspire them most to develop and write up.

EXTENSION

Pupils could:
- Draw Desmond's house.
- Imagine what would happen if Desmond was a teacher and list what might happen in an average day.
- Describe or draw Desmond putting up a tent, doing a science experiment, decorating a room, cleaning a car etc.
- Draw some things Desmond has made or owns e.g. a shirt he sewed or his bike.

Disastrous Desmond

Desmond is a disaster. Wherever he goes or whatever he does, mayhem and chaos follow him. There is no one on this earth that has as many disasters happen to him or her. A good day for Desmond is when he only has about twenty six disasters.

Your tasks

1. Here are a few examples of some ways in which Desmond is a disaster. Read the first few that are complete and then try and come up with some entertaining ways of completing the unfinished sentences.

Disastrous Desmond could get soaking wet in the Sahara Desert.
Disastrous Desmond could get muddy on an ice rink.
Disastrous Desmond could cut himself on jelly.
Disastrous Desmond could bruise himself ...
Disastrous Desmond could rip his clothes ...
Disastrous Desmond could get confused ...
Disastrous Desmond could trip over ...
Disastrous Desmond could crash ...
Disastrous Desmond could burn himself ...

Disastrous Desmond could get tangled up ...
Disastrous Desmond could muddle up ...
Disastrous Desmond could spill ...
Disastrous Desmond could break his leg ...
Disastrous Desmond could get lost ...
Disastrous Desmond could ...
Disastrous Desmond could ...

2. Draw a picture of Disastrous Desmond. Include as many details as you can.

3. Describe Desmond walking to the local newsagents, buying a newspaper and a pint of milk and then returning home. Try to include at least ten disasters in this trip.

4. Describe or draw what Disastrous Desmond would ...

- **have as his favourite holiday**
- **have as a hobby**
- **have as his favourite meal**
- **have as a job**
- **have as a pet**

- **have as his favourite type of shop**
- **have as his favourite T.V. programme**
- **have as a place he likes to sit**
- **have as his favourite song**
- **have as an outfit for going out**

Badge book

THE TASK

To design badges and award criteria for given themes.

INTRODUCING THE ACTIVITY

Pupils enjoy coming up with criteria for these made-up awards and then making a simple design for the badges. You could ask pupils to put the badges into a book set out like the Scout's and Guide's handbook. Encourage pupils to try and think of at least three criteria for each badge. Pupils will develop ideas more readily if they work in pairs for this activity. Really creative pupils might start to think of some badges of their own and realise that almost anything could be turned into an award with enough imagination!

There is an example of the type of critera you could make up on the pupils' page but here is another one to get them going!

Pizza badge

What you need to do to be awarded the badge:
1. Learn the topping of all pizzas in all the restaurants in your town.
2. Use the word 'pizza' every time you get cross or bothered for a week and keep a diary of people's responses to this.
3. Design a pizza that no one in their right mind would choose from a menu.
4. Persuade your mum/dad/carer to give you pizza for tea three times in one week.
5. Be able to tell three pizzas from their smell alone at the test.

Other ideas:
- Egg badge
- Homework badge
- Tea badge
- Walking badge
- Elephant badge
- Toast badge

Badge book

Your task

If you were designing badge awards for a club (like the Girl Guides and Boy Scouts have) for the following, what would your badge look like and what would you ask people to do in order to get the badge? Use your imagination!

- Exaggerator Badge
- Compliment Giver Badge
- Job Avoider Badge
- Politeness Badge
- Trickster Badge
- Laughter Badge
- Mender Badge
- Tidy Badge
- Get-away-with-it Badge
- Explaining Badge
- Bossy Badge
- Decision Badge
- Excuse Giver Badge
- Fantastic Friend Badge
- Liar Badge

- Boasting Badge
- Puzzle Badge
- Steady Hand Badge
- Tolerant Badge
- Super Imagination Badge
- Pretender Badge
- Fun Badge
- Balance Badge
- Cheerful Badge
- Nonsense Badge
- Sensible Badge
- Eccentricity Badge
- Listener Badge
- Calm Badge
- Organiser Badge

Here is an example:

Great Irritator's Badge

What a person needs to do to be awarded the badge:

1. Irritate three different people in the same day and ask them to sign a piece of paper that will prove you irritated them.
2. Make up an irritation questionnaire that explores what irritates people.
3. Make up three really irritating sounds.
4. Keep an irritation diary for one week and list all the things you have seen that have irritated people. You must list at least eight things.

5. Tell the badge tester what you think is the most irritating thing in the world and why you think it is.

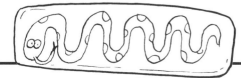

Modelling fun!

APPROXIMATE TIME REQUIRED: **10 – 15 minutes a task**
GROUPING: **Individuals, groups of four together for task 10**

THE TASK

To use modelling clay to creatively explore 3-D shapes and ideas.

INTRODUCING THE ACTIVITY

You can keep momentum going with these activities if you introduce 2 or 3 at a time, although they will work for a lesson if introduced all at the same time and pupils are allowed to choose the activities they would like to do. Obviously each pupil needs to be provided with a lump of modelling clay. Here are additional notes for *some* of the tasks.

1. You can help to inspire pupils by showing them existing pasta shapes.

3. You could ask pupils to explore more emotions in this way such as awkward, confused, embarrassed, bored, nervous, alarmed etc.

4. You can give pupils a selection of everyday objects to explore what patterns they make when imprinted on the modelling clay.

6. Give pupils a free rein by saying that an insect just needs to have six legs and three segments: head, thorax and abdomen.

8. An eight sided, fair dice would be an octahedron and it would look like this:

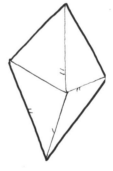

10. Pupils can play this 'game' as a four with two people making a model and two people guessing the nursery rhyme.

If pupils are particularly proud of something they have produced, you might allow pupils to enter their best two ideas into a 'competition'.

EXTENSION

Pupils could:

• Try to make different animals so that other people can guess what they are.
• Start with a disc of modelling clay on the desk and be allowed a certain number of cuts or prods with a knife so that another person can guess what they are trying to make e.g. make a fish in 6 cuts, make an eye in 10, make a shoe in 10, make a fork in 7, make a mouse in 12 etc.

Modelling fun!

Your tasks

1. Design a new pasta shape. Remember most pasta shapes are made from 'flat' pasta or a long string shape. Try making lots of different shapes and choose your favourite one. Give your pasta shape a name.

2. See who can make the most realistic nose shape!

3. Make some sculptures that you think show the following emotions: angry, excited, calm, confused. See if people can guess which emotion is which from the sculptures alone!

4. Experiment with making patterns by pressing different objects into the modelling clay. When you have a pattern you like, make a tie shape and give it that pattern.

5. Make a pencil top to go on the end of your pencil. See if you can make six different pencil tops with the same theme e.g. flowers, faces, food.

6. Make a leaf shape and put a strange looking insect on it.

7. See if you can make a pretty shape that you think would look nice dangling on a necklace and as earrings.

8. Can you make an eight sided dice that has an equal chance of landing on any one of its eight sides?

9. Make a shape that could be a fruit but that is like no fruit you know. Give your fruit a name.

10. Make something that some how shows one of the following nursery rhymes. See if anyone can guess which one it is without you telling them.

Humpty Dumpty	**Old Mother Hubbard**
Little Miss Muffet	**Boys and Girls Come Out to Play**
Hey Diddle Diddle	**Round and Round the Garden**
Baa Baa Black Sheep	**Ring a Ring of Roses**
Little Bo Peep	**Oranges and Lemons**
This Little Piggy Went to Market	**The Grand Old Duke of York**
Twinkle Twinkle Little Star	**Rock-a-bye Baby**
Jack and Jill	**Sing a Song of Sixpence**
Three Blind Mice	**Doctor Foster**
Hickory Dickory Dock	**The Queen of Hearts**

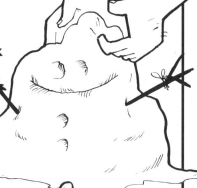

Your perfect remote control

APPROXIMATE TIME REQUIRED: 1 hour

GROUPING: Start in groups of four and then work individually

THE TASK

To decide what the buttons do on your perfect remote control.

INTRODUCING THE ACTIVITY

You could start pupils off in groups of four to help with inspiration at the beginning of this activity. Ask pupils to write a list of as many things that they can think of that they…

- like
- love
- hate
- are irritated by
- wish they had more or less of
- really enjoy
- try to avoid

You can also ask them to think of each of these in different settings e.g. at home, at school, in a town or city, in the countryside etc. This will help pupils to think of things they might choose for their remote control to do.

Explain the task to pupils make sure they understand the difference between the three different types of control.

The **dials** give information about quantity.

The **knobs** can make things more or less or not at all.

The **on/off** buttons can just switch things on and off!

Ask pupils to check that they have used the correct type of control for what they have chosen e.g. you wouldn't want to waste a knob control on making your window open and close when it is an open/close function and could be controlled by an on/off button. The knobs need to be saved for things you might like to vary in quantity, like temperature.

Tell pupils that their remote control cannot be changed once they have decided what it can do. Once pupils have finalised the functions of their remote control, ask them to draw a labelled diagram of it with a label describing what each knob, dial or switch does.

EXTENSION

Pupils could illustrate their remote control in action.

Your perfect remote control

This is your personal remote control and information receiver. It is no ordinary remote control. It is magical! You are going to decide what it can do.

This remote control has:

Three dials that can give you information about how much there is of something.

Here are some examples of the kind of things these dials could tell you:
- how much of a bad mood someone is in
- how likely it is that you will be able to persuade someone to do something
- the chances of you getting told off
- the likelihood of snow

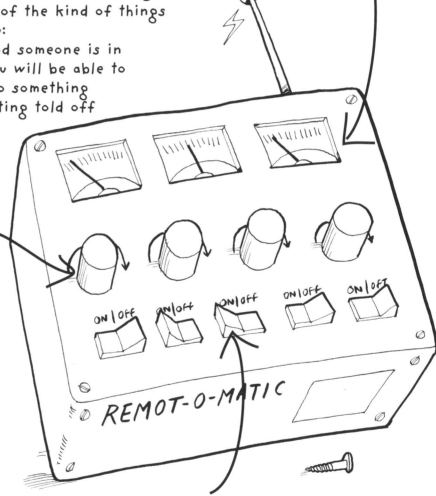

Four dials that can turn something up, down or off.

Here are some examples of the kind of things these dials could turn up or down or off:
- distances between places
- how difficult you find the school work in front of you
- gravity
- the size of your bedroom
- the sweetness of your food
- how quickly your hair grows

Five on and off switches.

Here are some examples of the kind of things these dials could switch on and off:
- someone's voice
- a lesson at school
- someone being nasty to you
- something that makes you fall asleep instantly
- something that massages you
- something that opens and closes something, like a shop or the school

A roog

APPROXIMATE TIME REQUIRED: 2 hours

GROUPING: Individuals

THE TASK

To create a new creature, describing it using the headings that are given.

INTRODUCING THE ACTIVITY

This activity is to encourage pupils to stretch their imagination as far as they can! Read through the sheet and check for understanding (particularly of 'acute', 'life expectancy', 'domestic', 'bulbous', 'natural habitat'). Ask pupils to complete questions 1 to 3. Here is some guidance on the numbered tasks.

1. Yellow food (pupils could list some yellow food), a fridge, candy floss for nesting, cheese, a nail file, a bucket, a toothbrush.

2. Pupils can be as imaginative as they like when drawing a 'roog' but they do need to acknowledge the details that have been given:

- Two short legs (diagonally opposite), two long
- Very furry head and underside
- Bald everywhere else
- Pointy ears
- Big round nose
- Tiny eyes that you can't really see
- Blue, green brown or pink in colour
- It might have splotch. In which case they would need to add some green warts on the bald patches.

It might look something like this:

3. Encourage pupils to think creatively – they could develop ideas in pairs for this.

4. Then ask pupils to consider the creature they are going to invent. Explain that their creature can be as quirky and unusual as they want it to be as long as it is entertaining to read about it. Try to discourage pupils from copying ideas from the roog's credentials! It usually helps to start by asking pupils to draw a picture of their creature. Pupils could label the unusual features of their creature. Then ask them to draft some ideas that could go under each of the headings:

- Fact File
- Brief description
- Food and eating habits
- Where to keep it

- Exercise
- Grooming
- Illness
- Dos and don'ts

If they use both sides of a piece of A4 paper, they will have plenty of space for pictures.

EXTENSION

Pupils could:

- Draw their creation to be included in a large picture of a zoo made up of all the class's illustrations
- Give the zoo a name and make a poster advertising it, or describe their visit.

A roog

Read about this crazy pet.

Fact File

Name: Roog
Height: 15cm
Length: 20 cm
Life expectancy: 21 days
Colours: blue, green, brown, but the most common colour is pink.
Most acute sense: sight (can see a pea from 300m).
I.Q.: 120
Natural habitat: bird boxes in cold countries.

Brief description

Roogs are very shy creatures. This is why they have only recently been discovered. They have four legs, two short (diagonally opposite each other) and two long. They have very furry heads and undersides, but have bald patches everywhere else. They have pointy ears and round bulbous noses. Their eyes are so small you have to look quite hard to find them

Food and eating habits

Roogs will only eat food that they are standing on and they prefer food that is yellow, like bananas.

Where to keep it

Domestic roogs are most happy kept in the corner of the fridge. They like quite luxurious surroundings and like a plentiful supply of candy floss to nest in.

Exercise

Roogs need lots of exercise (at least 6 hours of running around a day). Never try to put a lead on a roog. Instead, put a piece of cheese in your pocket and the smell of it should keep the roog close at hand, as long as no one else passes with some cheese in their pocket, which is a danger as roogs are becoming very popular.

Grooming

Never attempt to groom your roog with anything but a nail file. Use the nail file to spilt up the clumps of matted hair that always form on a roog's head.

Illness

Roogs are generally quite healthy creatures but do occasionally suffer from an illness called splotch. When they develop splotch, their eyes swell up and their bald patches get covered in green warts.

Dos

- Tickle your roog on his tongue with a toothbrush. He'll love it.

- Give your roog a bucket to play with. He or she will spend many a playful hour jumping in and out of it!

Don'ts

- Let your roog near anyone over 6 foot tall as it will bite him/her.

- Go near a lamppost as s/he will climb up it and refuse to come down until nightfall.

Your tasks

1. List all the things that are needed to look after a roog.
2. What do you think a roog looks like? Draw a picture of one.
3. Make up some more dos and don'ts for a roog.
4. Now invent your own crazy pet and fill in a sheet like this about your pet. Don't forget to include a picture.

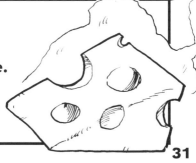

School exchange

APPROXIMATE TIME REQUIRED: **1 hour**

GROUPING: **Groups of 2, 3 or 4 and then individuals**

THE TASK

To consider some details about a made up creature and imagine spending a week with that creature. Write a diary for that week.

INTRODUCING THE ACTIVITY

Discuss the idea of a school exchange to ensure pupils understand what is involved. Explain that it is often done as a swap with, for example, children from France so that the children involved get an interesting experience of another country but at a low cost. It also means that the children get to experience home and school life in that country, which they would not be able to do if they were just on holiday.

Present the task to pupils by reading through the whole sheet together. Discuss the four creatures and then ask pupils to work in groups or pairs, to think of the kind of things that might happen at school, at home and in the world at large if they spent a week with the creatures. Consider all four of the creatures.

The following questions might help to inspire them:
* What might your creature do that makes you laugh?
* What might your creature do that might get you into trouble?
* Could you use your creature to get you out of trouble or get a reward for something?
* How might your creature's strange behaviour annoy the adults at home and at school?
* What might happen if you were walking around a town or a city?

Look at the tasks together using these additional notes:
1. Once pupils have considered all the creatures, ask them to choose the creature that they think would make the funniest diary for the 'exchange' week.
2. Ask pupils to make up a few more details about the creature they have chosen. They might like to present this by sticking the picture of their chosen creature on to a piece of paper and adding the facts as a list underneath. They could also write the diary on this paper.
3. Ask pupils to list the funny things that are going to happen that week and then to complete a diary. Encourage pupils to write in a chatty style and only include three or four sentences about one funny thing that happened, for each day. They can start from the moment they first see the remaining four creatures. You could read this example:

Sunday.

I really hope Vora didn't notice my jaw drop open when I saw the four of them standing there. I didn't mean to be rude but I had never seen anything like it! When I chose her she smiled, put her hand out and gave me a bucket of bags of peanuts. I shouldn't have worried about being rude because when I asked her if she thought we would get on, she said, 'no' and smiled.

EXTENSION

Pupils could:

* Draw some photos taken during the week.
* Make up some creatures of their own.
* Write the postcard that their creature might send home.

School exchange

Every year a coach load of strange creatures arrives at your school as part of the annual school exchange. Each year, every child in Year 6 chooses a creature to spend the entire week with. This means that the creature spends all day and night with your family, spending time at home, going to school with you and doing anything else you might do in a normal week.

When you arrive at the coach, there are only four creatures left for you to choose from:

Tregor

Tregor is always scratching and green bits often fall off his face and land with a loud thump. He is not very bright. He only really knows how to colour in at school. He is attracted to red things and is often found cuddling post boxes. He has to sleep with his feet in the air or he snores extremely loudly.

Gastina

Gastina is incredibly clever and has to be set extra hard work at school or she gets bored and starts taking over from the teacher. She is so clever she knows how to build a car. Gastina will only eat sitting under an oak tree. Gastina has one of the loudest burps you are ever likely to hear. It scares most animals!

Dave

Dave is incredibly strong and could lift two buses without trying. He cries really easily and once he starts, he can continue for days. Dave loves to play noughts and crosses and won't go to bed until he has played at least 20 games even though he has only ever won 3 games. Dave collects snails.

Vora

Vora is extremely kind and is always trying to win everyone she meets over by offering them a bag of peanuts. Vora often gets 'yes' and 'no' muddled up. She is scared of clouds but loves rain. Her favourite thing to do is change herself into a sign with an arrow on it to confuse people.

Your task

1. **Choose which creature you are going to spend the week with.**
2. **Make up some more details about your creature and write them down e.g.**
   - **how does she or he greet people?**
   - **when she or he sits at the table to eat, does he/she behave in a strange way at all?**
   - **does she or he have a strange way of walking?**
   - **does he or she have any other special or magical powers?**
   - **does she or he have any other really irritating habits?**
   - **are there things that make your creature behave in a strange way?**
3. **Write a diary of the week with a short entry for each day, including the most unusual thing to happen that day.**

Win the golden tokens

APPROXIMATE TIME REQUIRED: 2 hours

GROUPING: Groups of three

THE TASK

To design a TV game show for children.

INTRODUCING THE ACTIVITY

Start by asking pupils to consider game shows that they already know. What do the contestants have to do to win? What are the rules of the game?

Then read through the sheet with the pupils. Ask them to consider if they want a theme for their show. It might be a very generic theme or a very specific one e.g. one based on a fictitious character. They might also wish to replace winning 'golden tokens' with something else that relates to their theme.

Here are some examples of themes:

- circus
- colour
- monsters
- water
- the five senses
- Robin Hood
- animals
- fairground
- school
- plants
- magic, witches and wizards
- the world

Ask pupils to discuss ideas for each of the tasks. Stress that it is better to spend plenty of time considering lots of ideas at this stage rather than selecting an idea to write up as soon as they have one. Pupils can describe their tasks using these titles:

Task Number
Name of Activity
Equipment (draw a picture)
What the contestant needs to do to win the token
The rules of the task

Emphasise that it should be clear from what they have written, exactly what will happen in each task and how the golden token will be won.

Once completed, each group can present their ideas to the rest of the class. Pupils could vote on the game show they would most like to appear on!

EXTENSION

Pupils could:

- Draw the opening titles for the show.
- Make up some catchphrases that could be used on their show.
- Draw and write about the host of their show (wearing their hosting outfit) and label any special qualities or skills. They could also write the job advertisement that was written for this host.
- List the prizes pupils might get for the different number of tokens that a contestant wins.
- Attempt to make an approximation of one of their tasks so that other pupils can have a go at it.

Win the golden tokens

Your task

You have been asked to design a TV game show for children. The show will be about a child winning as many golden tokens as they can in different tasks. The more tokens he or she wins, the better their prize. You need to design the tasks each contestant will do to win the tokens (or not).

You need to design a task for each of the following:

Task number	Task	Examples and ideas
1	A task that needs a steady hand (or foot) to win	•a buzzer game •a balancing game •doing a tiny job with tiny tools
2	A task that needs you to have a good aim	•shooting  •arrows •swinging a ball to knock things over •getting things through a hoop
3	A puzzle	•word puzzle •maths puzzle •jigsaw •maze •understanding something written in code •finding a safe route across an area
4	An observation task	•look at a picture and answer questions about it •an identity parade •remake the potato head face you have just seen •draw a picture you have just seen
5	A task that tests your stamina, speed and/or fitness	•filling up a container with water with only small cups •a race against time •an obstacle course
6	And then after all of these tasks, you need to end with a chance for the person to win more or lose everything – based mostly on luck!	•toss a coin •turn a playing card •a pinball game •an animal going through a tunnel and predicting where it comes out

Promote your band!

APPROXIMATE TIME REQUIRED: **2 hours**

GROUPING: **Pairs or threes**

THE TASK

To produce a name, the title and design of a CD and a promotional poster for a band.

INTRODUCING THE ACTIVITY

Pupils see this as a very 'trendy' activity! Explain to them that many of the pop bands that they know will have had a lot of people working on their image (what the band appears to be like as far as the public are concerned) and making important decisions for them. Tell pupils that in this activity, they are going to be like these people and that they need to work very hard on the band's image and promote it effectively i.e. support the band to make sure it does well.

Pupils might like to start by considering existing pop bands and the images they have, although many bands change their image constantly! They can think about the bands they like and what it is they like about them. Whatever they choose, try to encourage them to stick to the image and themes throughout the CD covers and posters etc.

Some pupils might like to rename the members of their band and create a quirky image (with colours, emotional behaviours, animals, space theme, superheroes, etc), others may well follow the 'mainstream' images of pop bands. Remind pupils that they are not allowed to 'steal' ideas and names that they know already exist.

Explain to pupils that they are not going to make the CD cover CD sized (they are always reduced when printed) but that their designs do need to be square shaped. The promotional posters can be drawn on A4 paper and need to be as eye-catching as possible

EXTENSION

Pupils could:

• Produce a promotional poster for the new single called 'Upbeat and Interesting'.
• Act out the band's first interview.

Promote your band!

Dear _____, (write your names here)

Well, we have found four extremely talented youngsters: Georgie, Ali, Kate and Mickey. They can sing, dance and are totally up for being in a band so now the hard work starts! I think their image needs to be very 'pop' so they appeal to the youngsters. We need to start with a name for the band – something cool, of course, and then we need to get to work on a CD (this needs a name and image too) and the promotional posters. We need to sort out the outfits for the band for all photos: for the CD and the posters (their promotional outfits).

We have selected our seven songs (Flying, I Can't Stop, Is this Love? Dancing 'Till Dawn, Upbeat and Interesting, It's the best I can do, I'm Gonna Keep Trying) so that we can get to work on the CD cover design and the promotional posters. The band will be recording the tunes but we need you to work your magic to get the CD ready for sale and get these youngster well-known and in the charts.

Here is a photo of the four:

Get working!
I look forward to hearing about and seeing all your ideas.
Best wishes,

Sam Snithern-Jones

Your tasks

1. **Give your band a name.**
2. **Think of a name for the CD.**
3. **Consider the image of the band. Will they have a 'theme' that might show in their names, outfits, CD cover and posters?**
4. **Design a CD cover. This will have 5 'squares' that need to be designed:**
    - **A front – with the name of the band and the name of the CD and sometimes a picture of the band.**
    - **A double centre – often a picture of the band and some details about them.**
    - **The back of the inlay – this might tell you a bit more about the band and/or their songs**
    - **The back of the CD – often lists the songs.**
5. **A promotional poster – trying to persuade people to buy the CD and to help make their name well-known. This must include a picture of the band in their promotional outfits.**

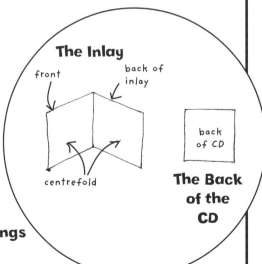

The Inlay

front

back of inlay

centrefold

back of CD

The Back of the CD

A revolting menu

APPROXIMATE TIME REQUIRED: 3 hours

GROUPING: Individuals

THE TASK

To make a menu that makes revolting ingredients sound delicious by using descriptive language typically found on menus.

INTRODUCING THE ACTIVITY

If possible, it is a good idea to start this activity with pupils looking at a selection of real restaurant menus so that they can see the language that is used to make the food sound wonderful. You can ask pupils to list phrases or words that have been used to make the food sound tempting and delicious.

When pupils are trying to think of more disgusting ingredients you could give them the following list to try and inspire them:

- body fluids e.g. sweat, snot
- insects e.g. beetles,
- illnesses e.g. chicken pox scabs, pus
- dirty places e.g. dustbins, gutters, rubbish dumps
- things that are not at all edible e.g. cement mix, wood chips
- cleaning products or materials e.g. a washing up sponge, mop juice
- things found in water e.g. water fleas, leeches
- food that isn't as it should be e.g. raw potato, mashed spaghetti
- machine liquids e.g. oil, grease, car exhaust drips
- things from animals e.g. rat fur, fur balls

Ask pupils to write their starters, main meals, drinks and desserts in draft form first. Pupils could pair up to try and give suggestions on how to make their revolting ingredients sound even more delicious.

This activity can take a couple of lessons if pupils aim to produce a quality piece of work. With younger children, it can be suggested that they make up just one starter, one main course etc.

EXTENSION

Pupils could:

- Draw the chef cooking in the kitchen and make him/her covered in revolting ingredients.
- Make a 3D fridge (by simply folding a piece of paper over) and draw or collage all the ingredients found on their menu.

A revolting menu

Your tasks

You are going to write a menu, in which, you make the most revolting ingredients sound as delicious as you can.

1. Add to this list of things that would be revolting to eat.

warts dandruff mould plaque	slug slime mud hair wire	toe clippings worms drain scrapings	ear wax leaf mould dirty lard hoover bags	spiders dust compost oil paint	grit brick dust soap old socks

2. Use the words in the list below to describe some STARTERS, some MAIN COURSES, some DESSERTS and some DRINKS made out of your revolting list. For example:

As a main course you could have:

A generous helping of lightly grilled leaf mould served with a fine selection of shredded slugs, seasoned with dandruff and succulent spiders, mashed, roasted or fried – it's your choice.

For drinks and desserts you could give:

a choice of revolting flavours, for example, wartberry.

Each meal could be illustrated and be given a name (e.g. Leaf Supreme, Hoover Bag Grill or Chef's Choice).

delicious enjoyable light tempting oven warmed delightful divine succulent refreshing sparkling tender rich in flavour fried	mouth-watering filling creamy topped with carefully selected traditional appetising a crispy coating special steaming hot speciality deep fried	popular classic delicate tasty seasonal super luxurious wide selection finest award winning spicy roasted shredded	supreme aged for flavour unusual nutritious freshly made juicy tangy lean exotic extra value choice grilled boiled	exquisite lavish crunchy rich tempting original recipe interesting blended ice-cool top quality prime mashed minced

3. Now give your restaurant a name and design, write and draw the complete menu. Don't forget to give your dishes a price. Think carefully about how you are going to set out your menu.

School report

THE TASK

To write an entertaining report for a given character.

INTRODUCING THE ACTIVITY

Read through the report with the class.

Ask pupils to list all the things in the report that relate to Penelope believing she is a spy:

- reading small folded bits of paper
- writing in code
- using invisible ink
- making periscopes and telescopes (one disguised as an umbrella)
- putting an ejector seat into her mother's car
- painting with camouflage colours
- learning many languages
- using gadgets with the computer (to run an 'operation')
- persuading pupils to tell her their secrets
- good knowledge of geography and being able to use satellite navigation
- considers herself as having lots to do
- using walkie-talkies and semaphore to communicate a strategy
- tapping out Morse code
- sneaking around the corridors and hiding in cupboards looking for anything suspicious
- talking into her pencil case to headquarters

Ask pupils to consider which of the characters at the bottom of the report they feel they could write the most entertaining report for. When they have chosen the character, ask pupils to list all the things that person might do to behave like the character they think they are e.g. if they choose the clown, they might list throwing custard pies, tight-rope walking, juggling, putting their head inside a lion's mouth, using a unicycle, making people laugh, being inside a big top tent, hanging out with other clowns, squirting water out of a flower broach, chucking buckets of water, spinning plates, wearing oversized trousers, braces and gloves, wearing colourful clothing, having a painted face, having an odd hairstyle, falling over, having things broken over their head …etc

Once pupils have composed such a list, they can start to think where they might include some of these things in different subject areas. Although pupils might try to include all subject areas, this is not essential. You might like to give pupils the target of including five subject areas and a general comment.

EXTENSION

Pupils can draw the character they wrote a report for and label any special features on their school uniform, school bag, pencil case that they use because of what they believe they are!

School report

Name: Penelope Link   Class 6Y
Authorised Absence 0 Unauthorised absence 0

Literacy

Penelope is a fantastic reader although she will only read small folded bits of paper. I have yet to understand anything Penelope has written as she only ever writes in code.

Numeracy

Penelope has very little interest in numbers. I have never seen her complete any work although every lesson she claims she has finished all the work but that it has been written in invisible ink.

Science

Penelope loved this year's light project. She made sixteen periscopes and three telescopes (one that was disguised as an umbrella).

Technology

Penelope refused to do this term's project on shelters but was extremely focussed in the 'you choose' home project where she built an ejector seat into her mother's car.

Art

Penelope paints everything using camouflage colours. This makes all her art work look rather similar.

Foreign Languages

Penelope seems dissatisfied with only learning French and is often found brushing up on Spanish, German, Czech, Danish, Latvian, Italian, Chinese, Japanese, Russian, Arabic, Portuguese and Welsh.

I.T.

Every time Penelope sits anywhere near a computer, she plugs in a variety of gadgets and appears to be running some kind of operation. I try not to disturb her.

PSHE

During a lesson on keeping secrets, Penelope spent her time trying to persuade everyone to tell her what their secrets were.

Geography

Penelope has a very finely tuned awareness of geography. She is a very skilled user of satellite navigation.

History

Penelope says that there is too much to think about at the moment to be worrying about what used to happen.

Games/PE

Last time the class played rounders, Penelope insisted her team use walkie-talkies to communicate their strategy for winning to each other.

Music

No matter what instrument Penelope is playing, she always taps out Morse code rhythms.

General

Penelope is a very intelligent girl but all the staff find it very hard to get her to do the same work as other pupils. She is often late for lessons, usually because she is sneaking around the school corridors and hiding in cupboards looking for anything suspicious. She is always talking into her pencil case and if we ask her what she is doing, she always replies that she is receiving updated instructions from headquarters. We are hoping Penelope will settle into her work more at high school.

Your task

Write a school report for one of the following pupils.
You do not have to include all the subjects.
A pupil that thinks he/she is:

- a circus clown
- a TV reporter
- an astronaut
- a famous scientist and inventor
- a character from a fairy tale
- a police man or woman

invisible ink

World's worst-World's best

APPROXIMATE TIME REQUIRED: 2 hours

GROUPING: Pairs

THE TASK

To fill in two completely contrasting application forms for a job and to act out two completely contrasting interviews for the same job (worst and best).

INTRODUCING THE ACTIVITY

Read the sheet with the pupils and check for understanding. Ask pupils to fill in the application forms first in their pairs. This will help set the scene and build up Jonathan's two contrasting characters. JG Worst's form can be really mucky! Encourage pupils to write really entertaining answers for JG Worst that really highlight how disastrous he is. Emphasise that JG Worst gives answers that the employers really do not want to hear, but that he does this because he doesn't know any better.

Then ask pupils to consider what would make an interview good and what would make it bad. Pupils can list all their ideas and then try to include them in the two contrasting interviews. Ask pupils to think up about six questions that will be asked in the interview – they can be similar to the application form or slightly more 'wacky.'

Pupils enjoy acting out the 'worst' scene and so can do the 'best scene' first to exaggerate the contrast. Tell pupils that although JG Worst is terrible at everything, he still actually wants the job, so he is trying hard – this makes it funnier and less likely to be a scene where JG Worst is just abusive!

Examples

Best:
Polite
Listens well
Answers the questions that
shows how he would be right for the job
Asks intelligent questions
Shakes the interviewer's hand
Smiles and appears relaxed

Worst:
Spills and slurps tea on interviewer's desk.
Sneezes in his face
Answers the wrong question – or doesn't
understand it
Says bizarre things
Gets muddled
Points out some terrible faults he has –
like being really clumsy – and gives examples of
what has happened because of this!

EXTENSION

JG Best and JG Worst could also be asked to do other things:

- be a receptionist
- read the news
- be a teacher
- be a waiter
- be a traffic warden
- be a TV Chef

The World's Worst and World's Best approach can be used for other ideas:

- lesson
- teacher!
- safety in a school or classroom
- apology
- invitation to a party
- queue

World's worst-
World's best

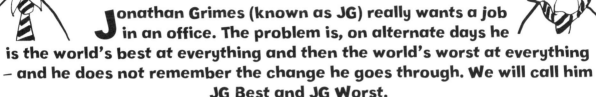

Jonathan Grimes (known as JG) really wants a job in an office. The problem is, on alternate days he is the world's best at everything and then the world's worst at everything – and he does not remember the change he goes through. We will call him JG Best and JG Worst.

A job has come up at Davidson's, a company in the town where Jonathan lives. He has received two application forms for the job (JG Worst and JG Best both sent off for a form). Both JG Worst and JG Best are going to fill in the form. As the company is desperate to find someone, both JG Best and JG Worst have got an interview.

Your task

You are going to fill in the two application forms for JG and act out both interviews. You can make this as funny as you like and try really hard to show a big difference between the two JGs! The interview questions can be similar to the questions on the application form but try and add some more unusual questions like:
If you were an animal, which would you be and why?
Give us an example of how you have coped with being really busy.
Do you like talking on the telephone?
Are you good at explaining things – give me an example?

APPLICATION FORM

Name: Date of birth: Address:
Qualifications:
Jobs you have had in the past:
Reasons for leaving the jobs you have had in the past:
Why do you want this job?
What skills and talents do you have that you think will make you good for this job?
Is there anything else you would like us to consider that will help us decide whether or not to give you the job?
Signature: Date:

Do a double take!

APPROXIMATE TIME REQUIRED: **1 hour**

GROUPING: **Individuals or pairs**

THE TASK

To rewrite the wording on packaging or containers to make it more entertaining to read.

INTRODUCING THE ACTIVITY

Read through the example on the sheet. Pupils can use the format given on the sheet or you could provide other packaging and containers for them to look at. Less able pupils can be given packaging with less writing on it.

Try and encourage pupils to think up as many of their own words for each section but if they really cannot, they can 'steal' the odd idea from the example given. Some pupils might prefer to work in pairs on this and some individually so a choice could be given.

Encourage pupils to keep the same sentence start or ending as the original in the example and just change part of each sentence to make it funny.

Helpful hint: The more mundane the words on the packaging, the easier it is to tamper with them!

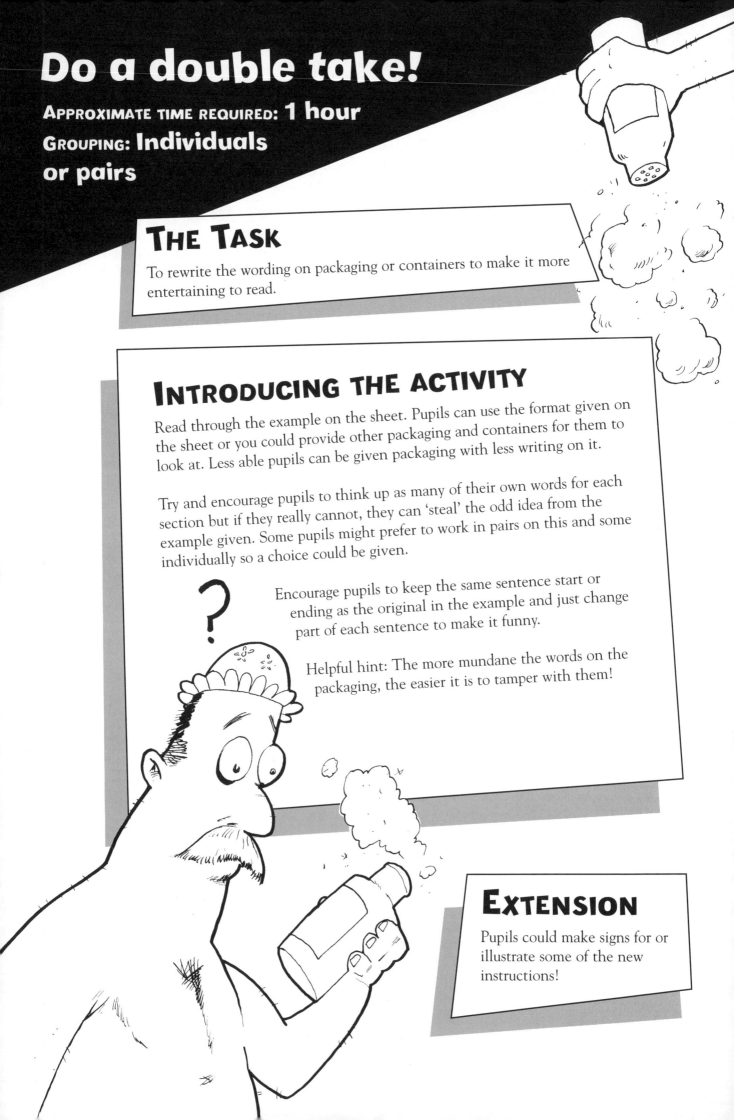

EXTENSION

Pupils could make signs for or illustrate some of the new instructions!

Do a double take!

Your task

Most of us never read the words on the side of the things we buy like shampoo, tinned food or packets of pasta, probably because it's rather boring! Do you think you could write a label that might make people look again or even laugh? Have a look at this serious example and how it has been changed to make it more entertaining. Either use Nelson's Talcum Powder or the words from some other packaging and try and write your own words that would make people look again and perhaps laugh!

NELSON'S TALCUM POWDER
Perfect for you and your family.
Nelson's talcum powder can be used after bathing to help keep your skin dry and soft.

DIRECTIONS
Sprinkle the powder directly into your skin and rub gently. For soft and smooth skin, use daily. To keep the contents of this container dry, close the lid tightly after use.

INGREDIENTS:
Talc, magnesium carbonate, perfume

WARNING
KEEP OUT OF REACH OF CHILDREN
Keep powder away from eyes, nose and mouth.

Nelson's are against animal testing and give money to research for alternatives.
No ingredients from animals have been used in this product.

Contents will settle after manufacture.

 Quality Assurance   **This Product had been quality checked for Nelson's.**

If you are in any way dissatisfied with this product please let us know on the Nelson's Careline. Freephone 0800 010101 Your statutory rights are not affected.

Produced in the UK by Nelson's Talc Ltd Nelsons Road London NW3 4RT

< 0432 7878 >

NELSON'S TALCUM POWDER
Perfect for large flea-ridden hedgehogs.
Nelson's Talcum Powder can be used after you have mown the lawn and preferably on a Friday after about 3 p.m.

DIRECTIONS
Pour powder into little piles on the floor throughout your house. This will annoy most people. For really effective irritation, blow on several of the piles to spread the powder. When you have finished, place powder pot on a high shelf.

INGREDIENTS
Ground dried slugs that have been fed on frozen peas, a red sock, two acorns.

WARNING
KEEP OUT OF REACH OF CHINCHILLAS
Keep powder away from people who move their arms about quickly.

Nelson's are against laziness and people who are impolite and give money to research what it is like to be an astronaut.

Contents might settle down and become better behaved after manufacture.

 Quality Stuff   **This product has been quality checked by Brian who hates his job.**

If you are in any way dissatisfied with this product we would rather you moaned to a neighbour. Their phone number might be in the telephone directory.
We have never understood what your statutory rights mean.

Produced in the UK by Nelson's Talc Ltd Bob's Place on the High Street in Wigan

< Nosey aren't you>

One glitful day

APPROXIMATE TIME REQUIRED: 1 hour

GROUPING: Pairs

ONE GLITFUL DAY

THE TASK

To make up meanings for made up adjectives and adverbs and then to make up adjectives and adverbs that replace given words in a text.

INTRODUCING THE ACTIVITY

Remind pupils of the difference between adjectives and adverbs. Read through the first passage. Discuss how the made-up words 'sound' and whether they seem like they would have a positive meaning or a negative meaning. Pupils may disagree. In pairs, ask pupils to make up definitions that would fit with the text.

The next part of the activity is about making up words to replace the adjectives and adverbs in the text. Encourage pupils to play around with the sounds of words. Often it works to mix up different sounds from the two or three adverbs or adjectives that have been given to make one word.

You might also consider discussing suffixes:
Suffixes for adverbs

> -ily
> -ly
> -ter

playing flassfully

Suffixes for adjectives – very varied but here are some:

-al	-ck
-le	-dy
-fast	-ty
-kle	-ry
-sy	-ful
-some	

EXTENSION

Pupils could draw several nouns that could be described by one of their new adjectives or draw a noun doing something in the way that one of their new adverbs describes.

One glitful day

One glitful day a piddy boy named George was walking lankerly to school. He hated school and he always became more and more deblimt as he got closer to the school gate. This day was no different from any other.

When he arrived at the playground, the other children were already playing flassfully. He never felt like joining in and so he sat limmily on the bench.

At that point a malonky girl called Daisy from George's class came bounding jobilly over to the bench. She started chatting knappily to George who was gleekful that someone had decided to talk to him. He smiled hestly. Today was starting to look flefter.

Write what you think the following words could mean:

glitful	_____	malonky	_____
piddy	_____	jobilly	_____
lankerly	_____	knappily	_____
deblimt	_____	gleekful	_____
flassfully	_____	hestly	_____
limmily	_____	flefter	_____

walking lankerly

Malonky girl

Your task

Make up words that would sound right to replace the adjectives and adverbs (in bold italics) in the following text (you can replace two words with one word):

One ***gloriously sunny*** day in the powerful and successful kingdom of Sarvare, Sir Dizzibell mounted his ***strong and reliable*** horse ready to go *bravely* in search of the ***fearsome and murdering*** dogswipe dragon.

Dogswipe dragons were extremely ***rare and hard to find*** but recent reports had implied that one such dragon had been eating villagers ***sneakily*** and ***without anyone noticing.*** The reason people believed that it was a dogsnipe dragon was because the bones of the ***poor and unfortunate*** victims were always found in a ***neat, little and organised*** pile. This was typical of the ***fussy and tidy*** dogsnipe dragon.

The problem with Sir Dizzibell, however, was that he was more ***brave and fearless*** than ***clever and able to do things.*** This meant that after five hours of ***quick and urgent*** riding across the ***pretty*** countryside, he found himself back in his home town by which time the 7 o'clock news was reporting how the dragon had been slain by a ***weak and feeble*** old woman who was out walking her dog. Sir Dizzibell went home and had a ***nice, hot and comforting*** cup of tea.

Gloomsville

APPROXIMATE TIME REQUIRED: **1 hour**

GROUPING: **Individuals and groups**

THE TASK

To write a description of a village following a set format with an emotion or a type of behaviour as the theme.

INTRODUCING THE ACTIVITY

It's a good idea to explore this idea thoroughly and inspire pupils before setting them the task. Take each emotion and explore what the village would look like when it was 'representing' that way of feeling or behaving. You could ask small groups to explore one of the emotions and jot down any ideas they think of.

The things that can be described in the village and about the houses are:

- Paths leading to houses
- Flowers
- Drainpipes
- Lawns
- Front doors
- Gates
- Soil
- Curtains and windows
- Flowerpots
- Litter
- Colours
- Rockeries

- Pets
- Weeds
- Sounds
- Cracks in paths or walls
- Paintwork
- Insects
- Cars
- Letter boxes
- Birds
- Ponds
- Walls
- Chimneys

Pupils can then list the ideas that 'show' the way of feeling that they are going to include in each paragraph. Then ask pupils to write their five paragraphs. Less able pupils might only want to draw the pictures and label them.

EXTENSION

Pupils could describe how they would run a 'Cheer up Gloomsville' campaign - with posters, questionnaires, and a list of how they might make the village a nicer place to live!

Gloomsville

The village of Gloomsville is probably the most miserable place anyone could encounter. Every single person, young or old, that lives in Gloomsville always looks completely gloomy and no one has ever been caught with the slightest glimmer of a smile, let alone laughing. The people of Gloomsville are mostly spotted shuffling from their cars to their houses with their hands in their pockets and their heads looking to the ground.

Not only are the people of Gloomsville miserable, the village itself looks completely downtrodden and sad. The row of terraced houses (Gloomsville Terrace), near the weed-infested village green, looks thoroughly run down. At number 1, a garden full of stinging nettles can be found in front of the door that is smudged with green fungi. At number 2 even the weeds in the window box droop above the cracked concrete path. Number 3 has a cracked window and no one has ever seen the curtains open. At number 4, soggy mud greets anyone who ventures up the path and at number 5, the moss covered path ends at a creaking door banging in the wind. No one ever remembers anyone living at number 5.

The village shop closed five years ago and its windows are boarded up and the drain pipe is coming away from the wall. When it was open, no one went in.

The village hall is never used and looks extremely tatty with its door hanging off its hinges and the paintwork peeling. Occasionally bits of litter swirl around the empty village hall car park.

Even the village sign, that has an 'O' missing, the greying 'V' barely attached and an off-white background, indicates the state of this depressed place to anyone that dares to visit this village. Overall Gloomsville is a place only suited to the most downhearted of folk.

Your task

1. You are going to write a description of a village that has one of the following ways of feeling as its theme:

confused   excited   bossy   angry   friendly   lazy   shy

Once you have chosen your emotion or way of behaving, write the following paragraphs:

a) An introduction that describes what the people that live in this village are like.
b) A description of a row of five terraced houses in your village.
c) A description of the village shop.
d) A description of the village hall.
e) A description of the village sign.

2. Draw a picture of the terrace and the village sign in your new village.

The Mystery of the Bronze Globe

APPROXIMATE TIME REQUIRED: 1 hour

GROUPING: Pairs or groups of three

THE TASK

To solve the mystery of the missing bronze globe, by finding clues in the newspaper report. To write a newspaper report titled 'Globe Mystery Solved.'

INTRODUCING THE ACTIVITY

Pupils may be quick to work out what happened: Mr Potson took the globe to use in the chuck the ball event because he has lost the log used in toss the caber. This log was found by Dee Halt and she used it in her bus shelter design. Ask pupils to write down all the clues that helped them to solve the mystery and what each clue tells them. You could ask pupils to produce a table like the following:

Clue	What it tells us
The globe is still on the statue in first photo on the page – taken at 2 p.m. The globe is missing in the second photo which was taken between 3.30 and 4 p.m. on 1st May.	The ball went missing sometime between 2 p.m. and probably 3.30 p.m.
Nearly all the village went to the play in the village hall.	Hardly anyone would have been around to witness the ball being stolen.
Mr Peter Potson was the sports coordinator for the event on Sunday.	Mr Peter Potson probably would have been the person to change the toss the caber event to the chuck the ball event.
Mr Peter Potson was working on the bus shelter at the time of the crash.	Mr Peter Potson did not go to the play in the village hall.
There is a ladder against the bus shelter in the crash photo.	Mr Peter Potson has a ladder that he could use to remove the ball from the statue
Mr Potson is a painter and decorator according to the advert.	Mr Potson was probably painting the roof of the bus shelter.
The ball in the 'chuck the ball' event was magnolia. The roof of the bus shelter is 'cream'.	Mr Potson painted the roof of the bus shelter a cream/magnolia colour and also painted the heavy ball this colour.
The centre of the bus shelter has been made using a large 'log.'	This was probably the log that was used in 'toss the caber' in previous years
Ms Dee Halt said she found all the materials for the shelter in the village.	The log supporting the shelter is probably the caber!
Mr Potson's address is 'The Green'. He probably lives next to the village green.	Dee Halt might well have 'found' the caber near to Mr Potson's garage – which would be near or next to the village green.

Ask pupils to sequence all the events and then to write a newspaper report with the title, 'Globe Mystery Solved.'

EXTENSION

Pupils could act out a court scene where Mr Potson denies that he took the globe, despite all the evidence presented to him!

The Mystery of the Bronze Globe

The village of Tidbury has a mystery to solve. Where did the bronze globe that used to sit on top of the millennium statue (in the middle of the village green) disappear to? No one can understand how anyone could have removed the globe without anyone seeing. Can you help them solve the mystery? There are plenty of clues in Monday's Tidbury Times.

THE TIDBURY TIMES

Monday 3rd May   40p

TIDBURY MAYDAY FESTIVAL KICKS OFF!

This year's Tidbury Mayday Weekend Festival kicked off at 2 p.m. on Saturday with the traditional maypole dance. Pupils from Tidbury Primary amazed the spectators with their skill and concentration. 'Each year I am astounded that they don't end up in a muddle' said Mrs Doreen Gray, one of the village's newest residents.

Like every year, the maypole dancing was followed by a play, this year called 'Spring Again', written and performed by the staff and pupils of Tidbury Primary. This, as ever, was extremely entertaining and had more or less the entire village in the audience.

CAR CRASHES INTO BENCH

On 1st May at about 3.30 p.m. Mr P. Anir crashed his car into the village green bench. Fortunately no one was hurt. Surprisingly, the bench remained undamaged, which is more than can be said for Mr. Anir's car. The only witness, Mr Peter Potson said, 'I was working on the new bus shelter when an

incredible crashing sound made me jump out of my skin. I am so glad nobody was hurt'. We had the mess cleared up by 4 p.m. so that it did not affect the weekend's fun.

NEW BUS SHELTER FOR VILLAGE

Designed by a local craftswoman, Mrs Dee Halt, Tidbury's new bus shelter has been put in place. 'It still needs a bit of work but should be fully completed by Monday'. She added, 'it hasn't cost the village a penny as it is a project I have done free of charge and

I found all the materials here in the village (even on the village green). I love the cream coloured tin roof. I am looking forward to people's reactions to it'.

SUNDAY SPORTS FETE

The sports fete run every year as part of the Mayday celebrations, was again a great success. There were a few stern words from the sports coordinator, Peter Potson as some people were found to be breaking the rules slightly. Daisy Green was disqualified when chewing gum sticking the egg to her spoon was discovered and Tom Bryant was removed from the area during the tug of war when he was found tickling his dad in support of his mum who was on the opposing team. A new event was introduced this year: Chuck the Ball where contestants had to throw a very heavy, magnolia-coloured ball as far as they could. This replaced last year's toss the caber.

Murder mystery

APPROXIMATE TIME REQUIRED: 1 hour

GROUPING: Mixed ability pairs

THE TASK

To work out who the murderer is from photo clues and to draw more possible photos.

INTRODUCING THE ACTIVITY

Pupils should be quick to realise that the murderer took all the photos and that anyone in the photo cannot be the murderer. They will hopefully deduce that Karla Klein is the murderer. The photos are:

Photo A
Cathy Caterham's family walking the dog along the footpath by the river.
The photo is taken from Riverview House (probably from upstairs).

Photo B
Gerald Godfrey in his house – so he cannot be the murderer.

Photo C
The Farmer's field and house – taken from Riverview House.

Photo D
Nigel Norton bird watching in his back garden, taken from Riverview House

Photo E
Foxglove House, taken from Riverview House.

Photo F
Inside Riverview House.

Ask pupils to make notes of all the clues that tell us what we are looking at in each photo.
Then ask pupils to use the information about the suspects and the map to draw four more photos that could have been taken by Karla. The photos can provide more evidence by either incriminating Karla or eliminating the other suspects.

Or
Ask pupils to choose one of the other suspects as the murderer and draw four photos that prove they are the murderer.

Where the photos were taken from:

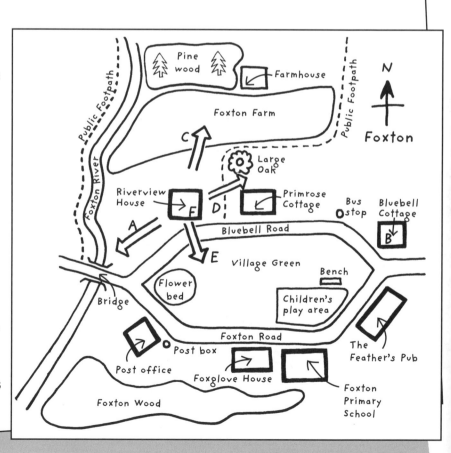

Murder mystery

Your task

There has been a murder. Can you help Detective Depiction? She found the murder weapon next to a camera and both had fingerprints from just one person all over them. Of course, she had the photos developed straight away. You need to see if you can help her look at the photos from the camera and work out who is the murderer.

Here are the suspects:

Gerald Godfrey
Gerald lives on his own in Bluebell Cottage and has done for about 10 years. He loves DIY and is always changing the decoration in his house. He often throws dinner parties. Gerald also loves fishing. Gerald knows all of the other suspects quite well.

Karla Klein
Karla has recently moved into Riverview House after 15 years of living in a city. She loved the house as soon as she saw it because it was decorated in such a modern way.
Karla only knows Gerald and Nigel from the village. Karla loves playing golf and tennis and is a really skilled player — especially of tennis.

Cathy Caterham
Cathy has lived in Foxglove House all her life. Her husband and two children (Felix — 4 and George — 6) also live with her. Cathy and her family are extremely busy and their house is always in chaos! Cathy loves painting. All of her family love going for long walks outside with their dog, Bruce, whatever the weather.

Nigel Norton
Nigel Norton has lived in Primrose Cottage for 47 years. He is a retired teacher and used to teach in the local primary school. In his spare time, he loves bird watching. He also loves gardening. In fact, both his house and garden are always well kept — and he often shapes his hedges to look like birds and animals.

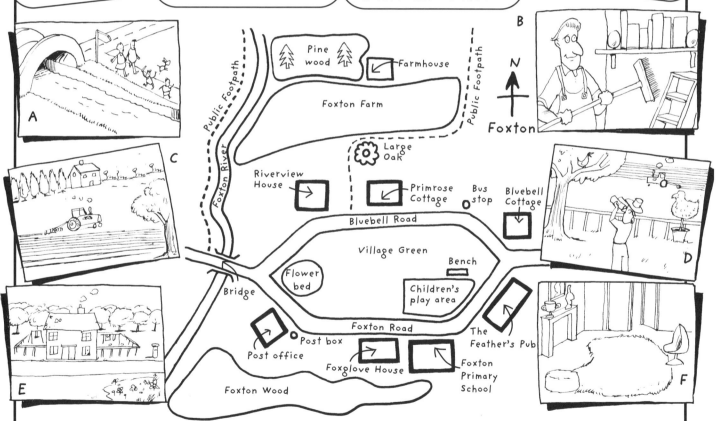

Try and work out where these photos were taken from and who or what each photo is showing. This should point you to the murderer.

Once you have worked out who the murderer is, draw four more photos that the murderer might have taken that either prove that they were the murderer or prove that one of the other suspects was not the murderer.

Place the pylons

APPROXIMATE TIME REQUIRED: 1 hour

GROUPING: Individuals or pairs

THE TASK

To find and draw the cheapest positions of pylons on the map to connect Astby Sub-Station (Point A) to Point B

INTRODUCING THE ACTIVITY

Pupils will need to tackle this partially by trial and error and partially by judgement. Pupils can work in pairs or individually, depending on the ability of the group. You can start the lesson by showing pupils how to draw the pylons and wires onto the map 1 cm apart. Pupils can use pencil so that they can rub their route out if their map gets too confusing. Point out to the pupils that 'K' has been used to represent £1000 to simplify the calculations.

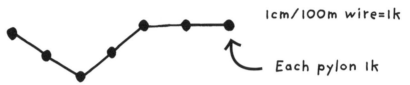

1cm/100m wire=1k

Each pylon 1k

This would cost 13K

And then give pupils some pylons to 'cost' for example:

This would cost 29K

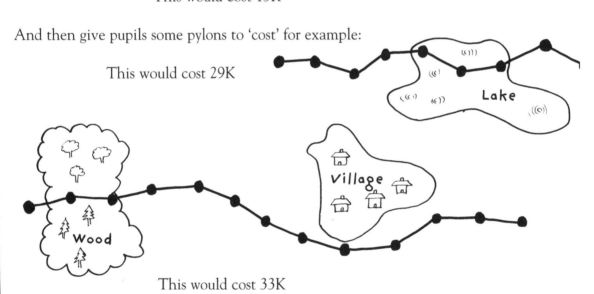

Lake

Village

Wood

This would cost 33K

The accuracy of different pupils' measurements and drawings will vary but the cheapest route is generally found to be around 40K

EXTENSION

Ask pupils:

1. How much would pylons in a straight diagonal line from A to B cost?
2. How much would two straight lines with a bend in the middle (east then south and south then east) cost?
3. What is the most expensive route you can get if you are only allowed to travel east and south in 'steps'?

Place the pylons

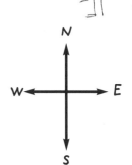

Your task

To find and draw the cheapest positions of pylons on the map to connect Astby Sub-Station to Point B using the table of costs below.

	Cost in £
Pylon on clear land	1 K
100m (1 cm) wire between pylons (this is the furthest gap you can have between pylons). Any wire between a gap less than 100m still costs 1K	1 K
Pylons that are closer than 100m (1 cm) to any village (because of the environment law)	2 K
Putting a pylon in any kind of water	5 K
Placing a pylon in wood or forest	3K

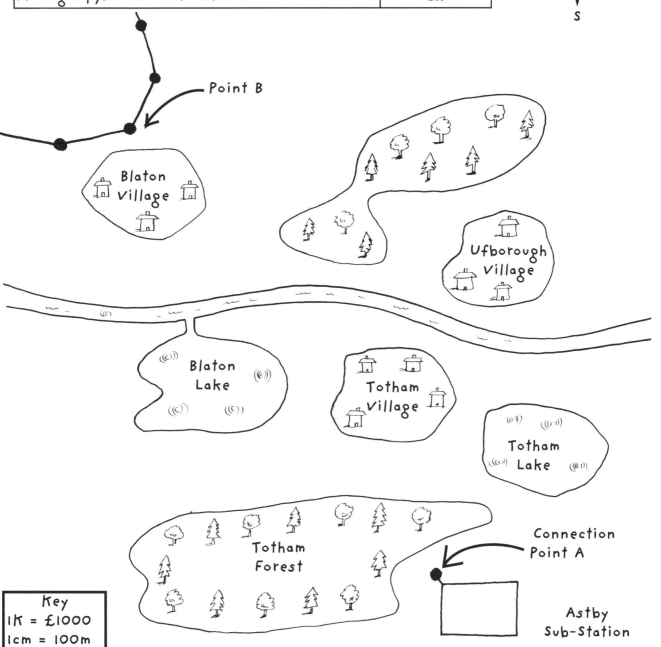

Point B

Blaton Village

Ufborough Village

Blaton Lake

Totham Village

Totham Lake

Totham Forest

Connection Point A

Astby Sub-Station

Key
1K = £1000
1cm = 100m

Four letters

APPROXIMATE TIME REQUIRED: 1 hour

GROUPING: Pairs

THE TASK

To gather information about the four people who wrote the letters.

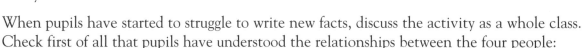

INTRODUCING THE ACTIVITY

Ask pupils to read the letters and work in pairs to try and write as many facts about the four people (Khallid, Paul, Ivy and Anita) as they can find in the letters. Ask pupils to sort their facts into 'very likely to be true' and 'likely to be true'.

When pupils have started to struggle to write new facts, discuss the activity as a whole class. Check first of all that pupils have understood the relationships between the four people:
- Ivy and Anita are twin sisters
- Ivy is Paul's mum
- Anita is neighbours with Khallid's parents
- Paul and Khallid are friends

You could also ask pupils some questions that they need to find clues to answer:
1. What relation is Paul to Anita? (aunt and nephew)
2. What is Kate about to do? (have a baby girl)
3. What job does Paul probably do? (car mechanic)
4. About how old are Paul and Kate's children? (George 4 and Henry 5 or 6)

Here are some facts to start them off but the list could easily be added to:

Very likely to be true	Likely to be true
Ivy and Anita just celebrated their 50th birthday	Ivy likes golf
Anita laid on a party for the both of them	Paul is a car mechanic
They wore the same dress to their birthday party	Paul is married to Kate
Paul and Kate were at the 50th birthday party	Anita and Ivy are allergic to nuts
Their party was on Saturday 19th August	George and Henry are Kate and Paul's sons
Kate and Paul have two children, Henry and George.	Kate and Paul are live music fans and like festivals
George is 4 and about to start school and Henry is already at school (so probably 5 years old as Kate and Paul have been together for 6 years)	Khallid is working in an office but is leaving next week to go to university.
Kate is pregnant	Josie is Khallid's girlfriend
Khallid is off to Nambridge University to study medicine	Josie is not going to go with Khallid when he goes to university
Paul used to play with Khallid when Paul stayed at his Aunty Anita's house in Winster	Kate and Paul are expecting a baby girl
Kate and Paul stayed at Ivy's for two weeks.	Kate and Paul have been together 6 years
Ivy looked after George and Henry while Kate and Paul went to a music festival	Tom is Anita's husband.
Paul plays guitar	
Khallid used to sneak through the fence to ask Anita for biscuits	

Go through the facts and discuss any cases where pupils have said that something is definitely true but that they have actually made an assumption e.g. Paul and Kate are married – they might not actually be married.

EXTENSION

Ask pupils to write five facts about one person. Ask pupils to write a letter from that person that would tell you these five facts about them.

Four letters

Your task

What do you think you can say you know about the four people who wrote the following letters and how they know each other?

32 Frank Way
Housley
Tuffolk
HS2 1PJ
Wednesday 23rd August

Dear Anita,

Thank you so much for the birthday party you laid on for us last Saturday- it took me back to when we were younger and our mother used to dress us up in exactly the same outfit with a large pink bow! Fancy you making us both wear the same dress! Still it was great to mark such an important birthday - people aren't 50 everyday!

I really enjoyed the food - you must have worked so hard to make it that good - still you were always better at cooking and better at avoiding nuts in recipes.

Things are settling back to normal, after Kate and Paul's stay. I adore my grandchildren but they are hard work. I was a little worn out towards the end of the two weeks.

Lots of Love ,Ivy

P.S. I love the golfing gloves - they are spot on - thanks.

---

102 St Swithin's Street
Winster
Tuffolk
WR3 6DP
25th August

Dear Khallid,

I hear congratulations are in order! Paul told me your news. I am so pleased that you have made it into Nambridge University. Time will fly and I am sure it won't seem long before you are making your mark on the world of medicine.

I saw Paul a few of days ago. I hardly see him now he is so busy with the kids and work. He still manages to play his guitar though! He had us singing along to all sorts of songs - if you could call it singing.

Your mum and dad always look well. We still chat over the back fence. It only seems like yesterday that you used to sneak through the gap and ask for biscuits! Tom is fit and well - not surprising really as I do look after him rather well!

Lots of love,
Anita

---

3 Neeth Terrace
Flag Street
Mansturby
Turrey
MY4 2 FT

Dear Mum,

Thank you so much for having us for so long. George and Henry keep asking where you are. Kate has to get used to doing all the cooking and cleaning again! She is a bit exhausted! And double thank you for letting us leave the boys with you for that whole weekend.

I hope you enjoyed your birthday celebration. I know we did!

I am back at work on Monday. I had just about got the grease off my hands towards the end of my stay with you. I had to fix Kate's car the other day - the brakes were a bit dodgy. I still have to paint the nursery pink!

George is looking forward to starting school. We keep finding him with his uniform on - even in this heat! Henry just keeps telling him that school is boring and the teachers always tell you off!

Take care and I'll ring soon.

Lots of love Paul

---

2 Bow Street
Sundon
Dosshire
SN3 2LL
24th Aug

Dear Paul,

I can't believe it. Two major bits of news in one week — I'm off to Nambridge and you're going to be a father — third time round. It's all quite different from when you used to stay with your aunty Anita and we used to play footie and make dens in the back garden.

I hear you went to the Buston Music Festival without the kids. That must have seemed a bit like the old days — when you first met Kate: it must be about six years ago now — yes?

Next week is my last week of work before I go. I will miss the people but not the phone or the computer! I am going to take a holiday — cycling round northern France on a tandem with Josie. Not quite her thing but I am hoping she will grow to love it as it will be our last time together for a few weeks!

Best wishes,
Khallid

Design a Park

APPROXIMATE TIME REQUIRED: 1 hour
(5-6 hours if the models are made)
GROUPING: Groups of 3 or 4

THE TASK

To design a park on a piece of unused land.

INTRODUCING THE ACTIVITY

Get pupils to copy the map on the sheet on to a larger piece of paper trying to keep some kind of scale e.g. 5 cm on the worksheet could become 20 cm on a larger piece of paper, changing the scale to 20 centimetres = 100 metres.

Try to get pupils to consider the scale all the time (though most pupils do find this difficult). The price list gives pupils a lot of ideas of what to include in their park but encourage them to include things not on the list (and make up a reasonable price). Obviously a theme park would cost far too much! The activity could be made easier for younger or less able pupils by removing the price list and budget.

Encourage pupils to carefully consider where they place different activities. They might need to think about:

- Keeping noisy and quiet areas separate
- How to make the toilets accessible to everyone that uses the park
- Making a footpath network that means people can get around the park easily
- Where more litter bins are likely to be needed
- The most sensible places for the entrances

Ask pupils to list all the decisions they made about what to include in their park, and why they put each activity where they did.

This activity can be turned into a more involved project if pupils go on to make miniature models of their parks. A large piece of at least A2 card could be used for the base (maybe reinforced with cereal packet cardboard). White card, tissue paper (makes good flowers and tree tops), tin foil, paint or felt tips and any other bits and pieces pupils bring in from home can be used to make a version of everything on the price list! Pupils could also design posters advertising the opening of their parks.

For pupils that make the park models, you could give each group a mark out of ten for the following:

- teamwork
- decision making (why they put what where)
- their model (maybe out of 20)
- their poster

EXTENSION

Pupils could:

- Draw some artistic impressions of what different areas of the park will look like.
- Design a puzzle area that would be interesting to visit in a park – treasure hunts, large puzzles, mazes, 3-D spot the differences, trails, riddles that refer to things in the park etc.

Design a park

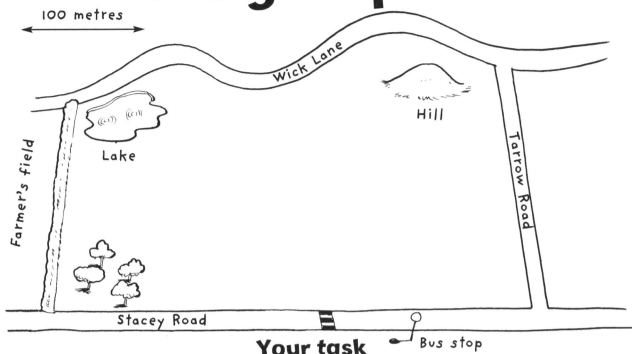

100 metres

Wick Lane

Hill

Tarrow Road

Farmer's field

Lake

Stacey Road

Bus stop

Your task

A local council has decided that it is going to turn a piece of unused land into a park for local people to use. As the map shows, most of the area is grass although there is a natural lake, a small hill and an area with a few trees. On the west side there is a farmer's field separated from the area by a hedgerow. Wick Lane is a quiet countryside lane and Tarrow Road is a quiet residential road. Stracey Road, however, is a very busy road and is on a major bus route. You will need to think about the following things:

- How will people get to the park?
  - How many entrances will you need?
    - Will your park need to be locked at night?
      - Are there things to do if it rains?
        - Have you provided facilities for people who may spend the whole day in the park?
        - Is your park an attractive place to visit?
        - Have you got things for all ages?
        - Have you got a noisy and a quiet area in your park?
        - Will your park get crowded in some areas?

The council has asked you to design the park. You have a budget of £10 000. The people who will work in the park are not paid from this budget.

Item	Price	Item	Price	Item	Price
100m fencing (2m high)	£40	Swing (for 3)	£200	Large shed	£200
100m fencing (1 m high)	£30	Slide	£200	Small shed	£100
100m hedging	£50	Climbing frame	£200	20m x 20m concrete	£100
A gate (2m or 1m)	£50	Litter bin	£20	Rowing boat	£100
100m of path	£50	Sign and post	£20	Tennis court	£100
A wooden bench	£100	Tree	£20	Football goals	£20
Fountain	£200	20m strip of flowers	£10	Bowling Green	£50
Sand pit	£50	Bush	£10	Crazy golf	£200
Toilet block	£300	Kitchen facilities	£200	Picnic bench	£40

Bundy's Activity Park

APPROXIMATE TIME REQUIRED: 2 hours

GROUPING: Pairs or groups of three

THE TASK

To re-plan Bundy's Activity Park and make suggestions that might help it make more money.

INTRODUCING THE ACTIVITY

Present the situation to the pupils and ask them to list as many things that they can think of that might prevent the park from making enough money. The kind of things that they might include are:

Position of each activity

1. The gift shop is tucked in a corner. Most people buy a gift at the end of their visit.
2. There are not many paying rides and they are all tucked in a corner.
3. The ice cream kiosks are not in places where people are likely to really want an ice cream (on the treasure hunt, right next to the swimming pool and tucked away by the gift shop).
4. The café does not have an outside area. This will mean people might prefer to picnic in hot weather.

Money

1. The entrance fee is too low.
2. There are not enough low priced things in the gift shop for children to spend their pocket money on.
3. The free playground has activities that could be charged for.

Other

1. There are enough free activities around to stop a person from needing to pay for anything to enjoy a day at the park.
2. The train stations do not stop at or pass by places where people could spend money or see things they might want to have a go on.

Ask pupils to consider how they would re-design the park with the aim of making more money. Advise pupils to consider which activities are likely to make the most money as they may wish to focus more on promoting these.

Tell pupils that they can:
- move the position of everything.
- add small features like sign posts, benches, shelters.
- put new path routes in place.
- change the prices of things and charge for things that are free at the moment.

Ask pupils to produce:

1. A map of their new park plan.
2. A new price list.
3. A description of any other changes or suggestions that would help the park make more money.

EXTENSION

Pupils could:

- Design a logo for the new park.
- Develop ideas that will persuade people to come to the park.
- Design the treasure hunt – what will people be looking for? E.g. letters for an anagram?
- Design a really unusual picnic area.

Bundy's Activity Park

Mr Greg Bundy is going to build and run Bundy's Activity Park. He has drawn a plan of the park and made some decisions about what he will charge visitors for entrance and activities in his park. Unfortunately, Mr Bundy's bank is very worried that the park will not make very much money if he builds and runs it to his plan.

Your task
Mr. Greg Bundy needs your help. Can you:
- **Suggest how he might put the activities in different places in his park so that it might make more money.**
- **Suggest price changes that will help the park make more money?**
- **Make any other suggestion that might help the park make more money?**

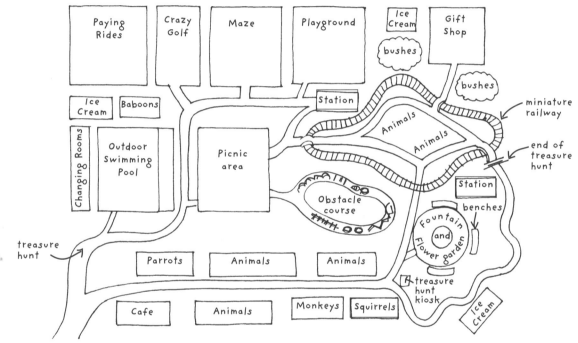

Here is some more information about the park Mr Bundy intends to build and open
The entrance fee to Bundy's Activity Park will be £3.00

AREA	COST	FURTHER INFORMATION
Outdoor Swimming Pool	Free	This is likely to be extremely popular and get really busy on hot days.
Paying rides	£2 a ride	Will include a merry-go-round, a ghost train, a haunted house, a mini roller coaster and a huge swinging pirates' boat.
Maze	Free	It will be huge but mazes are not usually very popular.
Playground	Free	Will contain slides, swings, a climbing frame, a helter skelter, a bouncy castle and a few trampolines.
Gift Shop	Sells gifts	Everything in the gift shop is £5 or more. It is hoped this will make a lot of money.
Picnic area	Free	Has many picnic benches.
Obstacle Course	Free	These are usually very popular.
Crazy Golf	Free	This is usually very popular and can get busy.
Animals	Free	A variety of small animals will be kept in cages throughout the park.
Miniature Railway	£2	The railway will have two stations. Once you have paid £2, you can go on it as many times as you like.
Fountain, flower garden and benches	Free	This place has been made for people who want peace and quiet.
Treasure Hunt	£1	You will have to hunt for clues on the route and write them down.
Ice Cream Kiosks	£1 - £3	It is hoped that these will make a lot of money.
Cafe	£5 plus	Will serve hot food.

Whigby

THE TASK

To consider a town's need for a bypass, to consider the best route and to run a campaign to push for the route that is decided upon.

INTRODUCING THE ACTIVITY

This activity should create a lot of discussion as there is no right answer. Most groups, however, do eventually decide on a northern bypass.

Ask pupils to consider the people described in the table carefully. They need to think about how most residents will probably prefer to have the road as far away as possible so that peace and quiet is maintained but that people who run businesses will prefer to have traffic passing by to provide custom. Some people might be genuinely undecided because of a conflict of interests. It is a good idea to discuss each of the characters after the pupils have filled in the table to check that they have not overlooked any details or considerations.

For parts 4 and 5, the class can be split into three groups:
a) for the northern bypass
b) for the southern bypass and
c) against the bypass.

Each group can then launch its campaign with posters and letters to the council and the local newspaper. Pupils could judge which campaign they believe is the most persuasive.

EXTENSION

For further discussion the idea of a rail link between Torwick and Harton could be suggested and hopefully lead to a discussion about public transport!

Pupils could:
- Draw some of the residents of Whigby with speech bubbles quoting what the pupils think each person would be likely to say.
- Write the newspaper article that announces the final decision.

Whigby

A building of a bypass to the north or south of Whigby has been proposed. Currently, the High Street of Whigby has to cope with extremely heavy traffic (lorries, cars and agricultural traffic) as it is the main through route from the city of Torwick to the city of Harton. The amount of traffic has increased considerably over the last few years. Whigby itself is a very picturesque village surrounded by countryside.

Mr. P. Smith	Resident of Primrose Cottage. He has lived there for thirty years.
Mr. C. Burgess	Owns and runs the Whigby Timber Mill. Heavy lorries from the mill use St. Peter's Road to travel to Harton.
Ms. G. Reeve	Runs Whigby Pottery. She lives in another village.
Mr. B. Howard	The owner of the fish and chip shop. He lives in a flat above the shop.
Mr. J. Porter	Owns Whigby Newsagent. Lives in New Road.
Mr. & Mrs. K. Potts	Have lived in the thatched cottage next to the newsagent for 15 years. They walk their dogs in Whigby Woods.
Mrs. P. White	Head teacher of Whigby Primary School.
Mr. & Mrs. F. Prood	Landlord and landlady of The Crown Public House. The Crown is a hotel and a restaurant as well as a bar.
Miss K. Fitt	Manager of Ratler's Restaurant. Lives on St. Peter's Road.
Mr. O. Nunn	Runs Whigby Museum. The museum is in danger of closing as visits to the museum are in decline.
Mr. H. Mayne	Vicar of St. Peter's Church.
Mrs. L. Haniford	Manager of Sonerby's Supermarket.
Mr. & Miss. B. Black	Own and run Wick Farm. Wick Farm is a livestock farm. Sheep and cattle graze in the fields that surround the farm.
Mr. D. Pips	Owns and runs Meadow Café. The café is sign posted from Torwick Road.
Mrs. J. Hoy	Resident of Hawthorn House. She is an employee of the Timber Mill.
Mrs. T. Wright	Manager of Whigby Library. She is keen to promote the use of Whigby Library by local residents.
Mr. A. Somms	Landlord of the King's Head Pub.
Mr. & Mrs. M. Lott	Live in Bramble Cottage. They bought the cottage two years ago after living in the city of Harton.
Lord and Lady Whigby	Live in Whigby Hall. They opened the house and grounds to the public five years ago. The grounds are famous for their beauty and tranquillity.
Mrs. N. Oliver	Resident of St. Peter's Cottage, next door to the church.

Your tasks

1. Make a 3-column table showing the names of the residents, a letter for what they think (see below) and a reason for why they think this.

A. Red: Probably for the northern bypass　　**B. Blue: Probably for the southern bypass**
C. Yellow: Probably against the bypass　　　**D. Green: Probably undecided**

2. Colour code the map of Whigby (page 64) A: red, B: blue, C: yellow, D: green.

3. Draw on your map a suggested route for the northern bypass and a suggested route for the southern bypass.

4. Choose one person from the village and write the letter that you think they would write to Hartonshire County Council – either supporting or opposing the bypass.

5. Draw a poster that the person you chose might have outside their house, campaigning for or against the bypass.

Map of Whigby

Key:
- ☐ Residences
- ▮▮▮ Pedestrian Crossing
- - - - Public Footpath

N
W — E
S

Meadow Lane

Wick Farm

Timber Mill

Many of the residents of Whigby work here.

Thompson Estate

This is a housing estate that was built just six months ago.

St Peter's Road

Meadow Café

Whigby Library

Whigby Pottery

Fish and Chip shop

Car Park

Primrose Cottage

The Crown Public House

High Street

Torwick Road

Park Road

Whigby Newsagents

Whigby Primary School

Ratler's Restaurant

Whigby Museum

Harton Road

Hawthorn Lane

Hawthorn House

Park

Most of Whigby's residents commute to either Torwick or Harton.

St Peter's Cottage

New Road

Lee Street

St Peter's Church

Bramble Road

Garden

King's Head Pub

Sonerby's Supermarket and Car Park

← Torwick

Harton →

Bramble Cottage

The River Wey

Whigby Hall Country Park

Hall

Whigby Woods

This is used by a lot of the local people for walks and picnics.